CONTENTS

INTRODUCTION

INTRODUCTION

1   This booklet provides guidance for pool operators and others concerned (including designers and manufacturers) on the risks associated with swimming pool operation, and on precautions to help achieve a safer environment for both the public who use swimming pools, and employees who work at them.

POOLS TO WHICH THE GUIDANCE APPLIES

2   The guidance applies to all types of pools used for swimming or leisure, *except*:

(a)   pools designed for medical or therapeutic purposes, (while in use for such purposes);

(b)   paddling pools; and

(c)   private swimming pools in domestic premises.

The guidance has limited application to pools which consist of segregated areas of rivers, lakes or the sea. The booklet's recommendations on safe design, working methods and supervision should be followed insofar as they are relevant. In particular, attention should be paid to the signposting of hazards; supervision of equipment; adequacy of written procedures, including emergency procedures; and organisation and training of staff. Specific recommendations on training etc will however have limited application in pools with unclear water and irregular natural bottoms. Reference can also be made to advice on risks in open water, published by RoSPA[1].

GENERAL APPROACH

3   Safety will be a fundamental concern of every pool operator. The approach of the guidance is to describe standards of good practice, as a basis for decision-making by management on what solutions will work best locally. The Health and Safety at Work etc Act 1974 (HSW Act) places certain general obligations on all pool operators; the following outline may be helpful.

POOL OPERATORS' RESPONSIBILITIES UNDER THE HEALTH AND SAFETY AT WORK ETC ACT 1974

4   Under the HSW Act:

(a)   employers have a general duty to ensure, so far as is reasonably practicable, the health and safety at work of their employees. This duty includes in particular the provision of safe plant and equipment, safe systems of work, a safe workplace, and the information, instruction, training and supervision needed to ensure safety;

(b)   employers also have a general duty to ensure, so far as is reasonably practicable, the health and safety of persons other than employees who may be affected by the way in which the undertaking is conducted. This duty includes protecting the public using a swimming pool;

(c)   any person in charge of premises, who makes those premises available to non-employees (either as a place of work, or as a place where they may use plant or substances provided) must take such measures as it is reasonable for a person in his position to take to ensure, so far as is reasonably practicable, that the premises, all means of access and egress, and any plant or substances provided are safe and without risks to health. The HSW Act definition of 'plant' is wide: it includes any machinery, equipment or appliance. This duty applies to protect contractors working at pool premises and the public who use the pool and diving boards, water slides etc.

Meaning of 'reasonably practicable'

5   The qualification 'so far as is reasonably practicable' means that the addition to safety which any particular measure will produce, needs to be balanced against its cost. Where the difficulty and cost are high, and a careful assessment of the risk shows it not to be significant, it may not be necessary to take action. In some cases however there will be things that must be done at all costs. No allowance is made for the size or profitability of the undertaking.

6   It is the pool operator's responsibility to comply with the law. This guidance should assist operators in deciding what safety measures are 'reasonably

practicable' in any given circumstances. Further advice can be obtained, if needed, from the local health and safety inspector (see below), though interpretation of the law is ultimately for the courts.

OTHER LEGISLATION

7 Reference is made where appropriate in individual chapters to other health and safety legislation imposing more specific obligations on pool operators (mainly relating to the safety of employees).

SUBJECTS NOT COVERED IN THIS BOOKLET

8 The booklet does *not* include recommendations on *water quality or other aspects of hygiene*. Sources of guidance on this subject are referred to in the third chapter and in the References section. Nor does it deal with *fire precautions*; advice should be sought from the Fire Authority.

9 Nor does the guidance deal with *liabilities arising under civil law*, on which pool operators should seek their own legal advice.

FURTHER ADVICE AND INFORMATION

10 Fuller advice on many subjects is available in the publications listed in the References section. Advice can also be obtained, as appropriate, from the organisations listed in Appendix 7; from the Sports Council; or from the relevant enforcing authority for health and safety legislation.

11 HSE is the enforcing authority at local authority-run pools, at school premises and at other pools (including leisure complexes) except where the main activity is the provision of residential accommodation. At pools which form part of residential accommodation (hotels, holiday camps etc) enforcement is the responsibility of the local authority, usually the environmental health department.

12 Appendix 10 contains a list of Regional Offices of the Sports Council and Area Offices of HSE. The address of the relevant LA enforcing authority can be found in the 'phone book.

CAVEAT

13 This guidance should not be regarded as an authoritative interpretation of the law.

SAFE DESIGN OF THE POOL
STRUCTURE, SYSTEMS AND EQUIPMENT

SAFE DESIGN OF THE POOL STRUCTURE, SYSTEMS AND EQUIPMENT

INTRODUCTION

1   Good design is the starting point for a safe pool environment. This chapter advises on how safety considerations (for pool users, and staff) can be taken into account at the planning and design stages for the pool structure, systems and equipment. Two aspects of design *not* however covered here are:

(a)   the pool water treatment system (dealt with in paragraphs 108-157);

(b)   equipment provided for bathers' use (in paragraphs 220-276).

2   The chapter draws heavily on the work of the Sports Council's Technical Unit for Sport (TUS), in consultation with architects and others experienced in recreational building design. Safety is one factor taken into account by the Sports Council when considering schemes submitted for grant-aid. Designers and sponsoring authorities are encouraged to meet the standards recommended here, and in other relevant Sports Council publications[2,3]. Where it is not reasonably practicable* to up-grade existing pools to the standards recommended, operators should consider potentially dangerous areas, and take suitable precautions, including additional supervision where appropriate.

STRUCTURE AND FINISHES OF THE BUILDING AND POOL

Stairs, lifts and escalators

3   *Design of stairways should meet the standards required by relevant Building Regulations.* Where a stairway is more than one metre wide, handrails should be provided down both sides, throughout its length. Stairways less than one metre wide should have a handrail on at least one side. Where a stairway is wider than 1.8 m, it should be divided into sections by handrails so that each section is between 1 m and 1.8 m wide.

*See introduction to the Guidance, paragraphs 5-6

4   *Suitable precautions should be taken to prevent people, particularly young children, falling through open edges of stairways or landings.* Where this would be a possibility, the spaces beneath handrails should be completely filled in by suitable material: see relevant British Standards[4,5]. If fencing is used, then in areas frequented by children the fencing gaps should not permit a sphere of 100 mm diameter to pass through. Horizontal fencing bars should not be provided, as these encourage children to climb on the barrier.

5   *Where, exceptionally, access is provided by a lift, or escalator, a safe installation should be provided:*

(a)   for lifts, the standards of design and maintenance required by the Offices, Shops and Railway Premises Act (Hoists and Lifts) Regulations 1968[6] are generally suitable; and

(b)   for escalators, guidance published by HSE on safe design, use and periodic thorough examination[7,8] should be carefully followed.

Children should never be allowed to play on lifts or escalators.

Access to the pool hall, and around the pool

6   *Abrupt changes in floor level in 'wet' areas should be avoided where possible.* Examples are staircase access between the changing/pre-cleanse/footbath area and the pool hall; or changes in level on pool surrounds.

7   Changing areas at a different level to the main pool hall are a feature of many older pools. Where the major alterations needed to remedy this are not reasonably practicable,* hazards can be alleviated by providing slip-resistant floor surfaces, handrails, clear tread markings and good lighting. These features should also be provided where steps are unavoidable in new designs.

8   Ramps can be used in place of steps, but they too can be a hazard when wet. Consideration should be given to the slip-resistance of the finished surface, and its gradient. A 1 in 15 slope could present difficulties when wet; wherever possible

ramps of a lesser gradient, with handrails, should be provided.

9   *Access from the changing/pre-cleanse area should preferably not be at a point on the pool surround adjacent to deep water (1.2 m depth or more).* Where this is unavoidable, a barrier rail should be provided to deter young children or non-swimmers from entering the water at this point. The position and extent of the rail should take into account such factors as the width of the pool surround, circulation routes, and the number of bathers likely to be using the surround at any one time.

10   *Where circulation routes to pool facilities take bathers near to deep water, special precautions may be needed.*

11   An example is where water slide access stairs are positioned near to deep water. Queueing near deep water is potentially dangerous, and should be avoided. In existing pools, barrier rails may be required in certain cases, for example, where the surround is narrow and young children/non-swimmers could fall into deep water, or supervision is difficult. Consideration should also be given to the route bathers will take between the pool hall entrance and the slide access point or between the slide landing pool and the slide access point. Where either passes close to deep water, barrier rails should be considered.

12   Where a diving pool is adjacent to a main pool or other water area, a barrier rail should be provided between the two pools.

13   *Pool surrounds and other circulation routes in 'wet' areas should be designed to avoid congestion, and to allow bathers to pass each other comfortably.* Although the Sports Council have recommended a 2 m minimum surround width for rectangular pools used for competition/training, narrower surround widths are provided in many pools without any serious problems. For new pools, it is suggested that surround widths be determined by considering:

(a)   how the pool will be used, for example, for training, or competition; and

(b)   the main circulation routes around the pool, taking into account access to facilities (water slides etc) and the number of bathers likely to be using the surround at any one time. Particular attention should be given to widths required at busier areas: for example, the entrance into the pool hall; surrounds adjacent to shallow water; the beach area of a leisure pool; and the route between the slide landing pool and the slide access point. (It will help reduce congestion if this route can be separated from pool surrounds.)

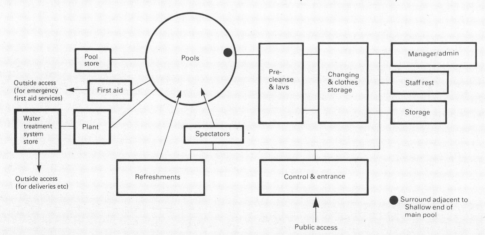

Fig 1 Good planning and circulation can ease management problems and enhance safety. This diagram illustrates a suggested relationship between the main areas of the building. Note particularly that:

(i)   access from the changing/pre-cleanse area should preferably not be at a point on the pool surround adjacent to deep water (see paragraph 9);

(ii)   storage areas for chemicals should be away from 'public' areas and accessible directly from outside (see paragraphs 118-120)

14   Equipment stored on pool surrounds is a potential hazard, particularly where the surrounds are narrow. Lane rope reels etc should ideally be kept in a poolside store; and pool covers either stored or integrated within the pool surround, or wall-mounted 2 m above surround floor level.

Finishes etc used in the pool hall

15   *Wall surfaces or features adjacent to 'wet' circulation routes should not be a hazard to bathers moving along these routes.* For pool surrounds bounded directly by walls, wall surfaces should be smooth for a height of 2 m, without any sharp edges, projections or abrasive textured finishes. Any projecting piers or free-standing columns should have rounded or bullnosed edges. In designs for new leisure pools, potential hazards from the location of features such as rocks, planting troughs, or water slide structures close to circulation routes should be carefully considered. In existing pools, management should consider whether there is any significant hazard of this kind which requires structural alterations.

16   *Floor surfaces to 'wet' circulation routes should not be slippery.* Slip-resistance is affected by both the surface finish of the floor and its gradient (for drainage falls, ramps etc). Various finishes are available with different surface textures and/or patterns which offer varying degrees of slip-resistance. Advice should be sought from manufacturers/suppliers and technical experts on the most suitable finish for a given situation.

17   A 1 in 24 minimum fall is recommended for draining away water. When used with a slip-resistant tile (eg '25 stud' ceramic tiles) this amount of fall should not create difficulties.

18   *Suitably-toughened glazing - as specified in British Standard 6206[9] - should be used adjacent to 'wet' circulation routes:* for example, in low level windows, or glazed screens between viewing areas and the pool surround. This will reduce the risk of injury to bathers (eg from collisions), or of breakages caused by the movement of pool equipment.

19   If the pool is used for water polo, windows need protection against ball impact: for example, by the use of impact-resisting polycarbonate, netting, or other method.

20   *Consideration should be given to the use of building materials and systems to help reduce noise and reverberation.* Excessive noise is distracting to pool users and lifeguards. The impervious finishes, glazing, and water surfaces commonly found in swimming pool halls are all efficient reflectors of sound and increase the acoustic problem.

21   The Chartered Institution of Building Services Engineers (CIBSE) have recommended design criteria for background noise levels[10]. Various suitable materials are obtainable, including sound-absorbing blocks (made from concrete or other materials) or proprietary tiles, which may be used in suspended ceilings or similar structures. Further information is contained in a British Standards Code of Practice[11].

Access into the pool

22   *Pool access steps should allow for easy and safe entry to, and exit from, the water.* Fewer stepped entry points may be needed where the pool edge is of the deck-level type (rather than the conventional overflow channel): many bathers (including disabled people) find it easier, with a deck-level pool, to enter and leave directly from the pool side. It is suggested that steps are provided in the following locations:

(a)   for rectangular main pools, at each end of the pool tank in each side wall, I m approximately from the pool tank end walls. Additional steps can be provided mid-way along the side walls, if required;

(b)   for learner pools, where the tank is rectangular, across the full width of the pool. For irregular pools the steps can for example be designed to follow the shape of the tank;

(c)   for training pools, the steps should be positioned on the long sides and recessed behind the pool tank walls, so as not to disrupt or endanger swimmers using the length of the pool for training;

(d) for leisure pools with freeboards, steps allowing access/egress to and from all water areas should be 10 m to 15 m apart;

(e) for slide landing pools, the exit should be at the end opposite to the entry point from the slide.

23 Barrier rails should be provided where necessary to prevent bathers from jumping onto pool access steps from surrounds.

The pool tank

24 *The pool edge should be colour-contrasted with the pool tank/water.* The edge should be clearly visible to bathers in the water. Equally, bathers on surrounds should be able to see the edge clearly, to avoid hitting it when diving or jumping in. This is particularly important for deck-level pools, where the pool edge may be partially submerged. Either the pool surround as a whole can be colour-contrasted with the pool tank/water, or the pool edge can be picked out with a contrasting colour.

25 At many leisure pools, however, the pool tank slopes gently from a beach area to deeper water, without any change in colour or surface finish texture. In such circumstances there should be no need to highlight the water's edge, providing there are no upstands or small steps between the pool and surround.

26 *Steps giving access into the pool should be easy and safe to use.* In particular, they should:

(a) have handrails, and slip-resistant treads, firmly fixed, to the surround and tank walls without excessive movement; and

(b) be designed to prevent fingers or other parts of the body from being trapped between the treads and the tank wall.

27 Wide steps used for access to learner pools or shallow water should have shallow risers (about 150-160 mm) to allow easy use by young children, or by a parent carrying a child. The leading edge of each step should be colour-contrasted for visibility. All steps below water level should also meet these standards.

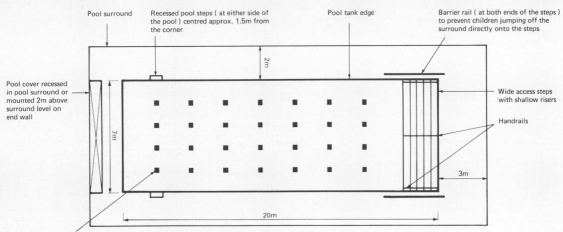

Fig 2 Typical layout and dimensions for learner/training pool, including wide steps for access (see paragraphs 22 and 26-27). Note also the recessed steps at the other end of the pool (see paragraph 22(c)); the barrier rails (paragraph 23); and the pool cover (paragraph 14). NB The steps indicated above are positioned for a learner pool. For a learner/training pool, the steps should be recessed along the side of the pool, see paragraph 22(c).

28 *The profile of the bottom of the pool tank should not be a hazard to bathers in the water or to those jumping or diving in from surrounds or from a diving board.* Steep gradients or abrupt changes in level should be avoided. Serious injuries have been suffered by divers hitting the inclined pool bottom between changes in level.

29 For rectangular main pools, the Sports Council have recommended a number of possible profiles, with water depths ranging from 2 m or 1.8 m deep water to 900 mm shallow water, and with gradients of not more than 1 in 15. In other types of pool, such as irregular leisure pools, the profile will depend on the pool layout and features present. Abrupt changes in depth should be avoided where possible. Steep gradients also increase the risk of slipping in shallow water areas; a maximum gradient of 1 in 15 is recommended for depths up to 1.5 m. Possible profiles are illustrated below.

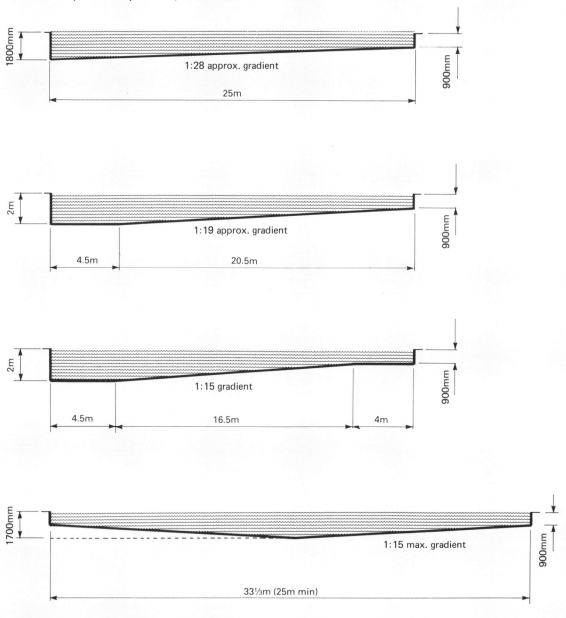

Fig 3 Pool tank profiles

30 In all pools, any sudden changes in depth should be indicated by signs clearly visible from all parts of the pool hall. Colour-contrasted or patterned finishes on inclined surfaces, to highlight changes in level, should be considered where appropriate.

31 *The pool tank finishes should not be slippery underfoot.* A slip-resistant and non-abrasive surface should be provided in the following locations:

(a) at the shallow end of main pools used for competition/training (the floor area up to 1.2 m from the end wall);

(b) for learner pools, the pool bottom, including steps;

(c) for leisure pools, the beach area, shallow areas up to 1.5 m water depth, and any areas where bathers may congregate when a wave machine is operating (particularly if the pool bottom has a gradient of 1 in 15 or more).

32 *The pool tank should have no sharp edges or projections which could cause injury.* The advice in paragraph 15 should be followed, as appropriate.

33 *Openings, recesses, ledges or grab rails, designed as part of the pool tank, should not be a hazard to bathers in the pool or those jumping in from surrounds.*

34 Wave machine openings, sumps, or inlets and outlets of the pool water circulation system should have suitable protective covers or grilles. They should be designed to prevent limbs and fingers getting trapped. Undue suction should not be created at the opening position, which could result in a body being held against the grille; and there should be no exposed sharp edges. This is particularly important in areas of moving water.

35 Grab rails, where provided, should preferably be recessed into the pool tank walls, rather than projecting into the tank. It should not be possible for limbs to become trapped between the grab rail and the rear wall of the recess.

36 There are reported cases of bathers jumping or diving in and striking projecting rest ledges. Ledges should preferably be recessed flush with the pool tank walls; alternatively, they can be colour-contrasted and notices displayed warning of their presence.

SAFETY SIGNS

37 The content, design and location of warning notices need to be carefully considered as part of a safe pool environment. Particularly important are:

(a) clear marking of the depth of water, especially of shallow and deep ends;

(b) signs showing areas where it is safe to swim, or to dive (and indicating any sudden changes in depth which could pose a hazard); and

(c) suitable instructions on the safe use of diving or other equipment.

38 Signs should comply with the Safety Signs Regulations 1980[12]. Pictorial signs are recommended, where appropriate, supplemented as necessary by text. Signs can be displayed not only in the pool area, but in changing rooms or passages where pool users may queue. See Appendix 2 for references to the Regulations, and for examples of suitable signs prepared by a Working Party of RoSPA's National Water Safety Committee. RoSPA's aim is to develop and standardise a more extensive range of signs, complying with the Regulations; signs are available from RoSPA, at the address listed in Appendix 7.

HEATING, VENTILATION AND AIR-CONDITIONING SYSTEMS

39 *These systems need to be considered together.* The quality of the pool environment - temperature, humidity, and air purity - may significantly influence safety, through its effects on the concentration and efficiency of pool users and of lifeguards. Also, excess humidity can corrode the pool structure and finishes, and magnify risks associated with electrical fittings. A safe environment depends on good standards of design and installation of the relevant systems and equipment. When new installations are commissioned and balanced, they should be assessed to ensure that they achieve the original design specification.

Heating

40   *The swimming pool hall, changing rooms and other occupied areas should be maintained at a comfortable temperature.* A maximum of around 27°C for water, with the air temperature about 1°C higher to avoid excess condensation, may be most suitable. (Where significantly higher temperatures are maintained - for example, in some leisure or learner pools - possible adverse effects on lifeguards' capacity to remain alert for long periods, will need to be taken into account, when deciding on maximum duty spells: see paragraph 201).

41   *Heating and associated fuel storage and delivery systems should be of sound construction, and competently installed.* Information on automatic controls for steam and hot water boilers has been published by HSE[13], and by British Gas[14]. Where automatic tank heating elements are provided, suitable controls should ensure that they do not operate unless immersed in fuel oil. Further guidance has been published by HSE[15].

42   *Fuel oil tanks if above ground should be contained within a suitably bunded area capable of holding 110 per cent of the contents of the largest tank within the bund.* Drain valves should preferably not be fitted in bund walls. (See also paragraph 86).

43   *Separate, suitably fire-resistant storage should be provided for liquefied petroleum gas (LPG), or for highly flammable liquids.* Advice on each has been published by HSE[16,17,18].

Ventilation

44   *Effective, draught-free ventilation should be provided throughout the building by natural or artificial means,* eg by air conditioning systems. At higher temperatures, humidity will rise - the warmer air retaining more moisture, and the pool water evaporating more rapidly. Humidity and air movement should be balanced to achieve comfortable conditions; air movement being the easier one to control.

45   Windows and air intakes for ventilation systems should not be installed close to areas where disinfection chemicals are stored, or where ventilation pipes from water treatment or other equipment discharges. The air intakes and discharges of air-conditioning or ventilation systems should also be effectively separated. Careful consideration should be given to any air re-circulation system where pool hall air is to be utilised, as re-circulation of contaminants could increase overall contamination levels. Further advice has been published by CIBSE[10]; the Sports Council[19,20]; and the American Conference of Governmental Industrial Hygienists[21]. See also the relevant British Standards[22,23].

LIGHTING

46   Adequate natural or artificial lighting should be provided and maintained throughout the building. Guidance has been published by CIBSE[24,25] and by the International Commission on Illumination[26].

47   External glazing, and artificial lighting, should together ensure that:

(a)   lifeguards and bathers are not subjected to excessive glare, or reflections from the pool water. Nor should there be excessive solar gain. Where such problems arise in existing installations, suitable blinds, screens or tinted glazing should be used;

(b)   the whole of the pool base, and underwater swimmers, are easily visible to lifeguards and bathers;

(c)   emergency lighting is provided where necessary to ensure that emergency evacuation procedures can be carried out safely in the event of a general power failure. It should be installed and operated in accordance with the relevant British Standard[27].

48   Where illumination is less than fully adequate, extra supervision may be needed (see paragraph 201).

49   Breakable light fittings should preferably not be used above the water. Where such fittings are provided in existing pools, they should be protected so that they cannot be damaged accidentally. Light fittings should be:

(a)   designed with ease of maintenance

in mind. This is particularly applicable to light fittings in the pool hall and especially any over the pool water;

(b)   suitably cased and sealed against moisture ingress and corrosion from contaminants in the atmosphere.

ELECTRICAL INSTALLATIONS AND EQUIPMENT

50   The various risks from electricity - shock, burns, fire or explosions - can be magnified by the wet and corrosive conditions in pools and associated areas. Designers need to be aware of the various risks, and take due precautions.

General precautions

51   If the electricity supply to the pool complex is to be a protective multiple earth (PME) system, the electricity supply authority should be consulted about earthing, and the requirements for protective bonding of the services, structures and other extraneous conductive parts of the complex which are not part of the electrical installation.

52   Suitably-placed isolation facilities (eg switchfuses with locking facilities) should be provided for all equipment, including lighting, so that it can be isolated for routine maintenance, such as replacing lamps. See relevant British Standards[28,29].

53   Fixed electrical installations should be designed and installed to the standards in the current edition of Regulations for Electrical Installations (where these apply), published by the Institution of Electrical Engineers[30]. These standards should also be followed whenever an existing installation is modified, extended or altered in any way.

54   Where possible, installations should be sited in areas inaccessible to the public: ideally, behind locked doors. All conductors and parts of equipment operating at voltages above 650 V must be sited in locked enclosures with power interlocks, in accordance with British Standard 5304[31] or the relevant equipment standard, so that access cannot be obtained unless they are isolated from the supply. (See paragraph 106 for advice

on conductors operating at voltages of 650 V or less).

55   Socket outlets installed to provide power for portable equipment should be of the industrial pattern set out in British Standard 4343[32]. All outlets operating at voltages in excess of 50 V AC or 120 V DC should be supplied with a suitably-rated residual current circuit-breaker with a rated tripping current not exceeding 30 milliamps. Socket outlets may be protected individually or in groups not exceeding six socket outlets in total. Sufficient outlets should be provided to avoid the need for possibly dangerous trailing extension leads.

Precautions in 'wet' areas

56   Every effort should be made to avoid locating socket outlets and other fixed installations in 'wet' areas. Where this is unavoidable, guidance published by the International Electrotechnical Committee[33] should be followed. Equipment to be used where there is a possibility of condensation, splashing or jetting by hoses, should be selected with an appropriate IP rating, as set out in British Standard 5490[34]: for example, IP 43 or IP 55. Particular care is needed when installing lighting under water.

57   Air-powered or self-contained 12 V battery operated portable equipment should, wherever possible, be used in areas which are wet, confined or conductive (eg the interior of a boiler where maintenance staff may have to crawl in close contact with earthed metalwork). If it is essential to use electrically-powered equipment near the pool, the equipment should be designed to withstand immersion. If this is impossible, it should be used only when the pool is empty of people, and should be fitted with some form of restraint (eg a rope or chain sliding along a secure wire fixed to the pool enclosure, of a length permitting operation of the equipment, but short enough to prevent it falling into the pool). Alternatively, barriers should be erected around the pool to prevent accidental immersion.

58   In addition it is recommended that:

(a)   earth monitoring should be provided

for all 415 V AC 3 phase equipment which requires protective (earth) conductors. (Where BS 4343[32] plugs and sockets are used, there are difficulties in obtaining units with the extra earth monitoring pin in 16 amp and 32 amp ranges);

(b)   all 240 V AC equipment should be supplied via a socket fed from a residual current circuit-breaker. The rated trip setting should not exceed 30 mA (in accordance with BS 4293[35]). The unit will need to be rated for the current capacity of the circuit;

(c)   mains-operated audio equipment should not be allowed on the poolside - it should be sited in a dry room away from the pool;

(d)   nor should sun-beds be placed beside the pool, where splashing could pose an electrical hazard;

(e)   hand lamps should be selected in accordance with HSE Guidance Note PM 38[36]. In wet or confined spaces, the use of battery-operated torches or lanterns is strongly advised. However, if temporary lighting supplied from the mains is used it should operate at 24 V or 50 V supplied from a safety isolating transformer made to British Standard 3535[37] or an equivalent standard;

(f)   portable electrical equipment operating at 110 V (or lower voltages) should be supplied from a safety isolating transformer complying with BS 3535[37]. The centre-tap of the transformer secondary winding should normally be earthed.

Further guidance has been published by HSE[38].

Precautions in potentially explosive atmospheres

59   Special precautions are needed where electrical equipment is to be used in a potentially explosive atmosphere, for example close to an electrolytic sodium hypochlorite generator which produces hydrogen as a by-product. The equipment should be selected, and installed, and the area or room zoned in accordance with relevant British Standards[39,40]. Published HSE guidance[41] should be followed, as appropriate.

MAINTENANCE REQUIREMENTS, AND SAFE WORKING PRACTICES (EXCEPT WATER TREATMENT)

MAINTENANCE REQUIREMENTS, AND SAFE WORKING PRACTICES (EXCEPT WATER TREATMENT)

INTRODUCTION

60   This chapter advises on maintenance requirements for swimming pool structures, engineering systems and equipment. It gives guidance on how associated work activities can be carried out safely. (Guidance on water treatment systems is however given under 'The pool water treatment system' below.)

61   On many of the work activities mentioned in this chapter, HSE has published more detailed guidance, applicable to all types of premises. The chapter concentrates mainly on risks which are specific to swimming pools, or which may be aggravated by conditions - eg wet surfaces, or humidity - found in swimming pools. This means that some important areas are dealt with only very generally. Operators should seek fuller advice, as needed, from the publications listed in the References section, or from the relevant enforcing authority for health and safety legislation (see Introduction to the Guidance paragraph 11).

MAINTENANCE: GENERAL REQUIREMENTS

62   Regular and correct maintenance of buildings, plant and electrical equipment is important in ensuring the safety and health of pool users, and employees. Designs (or manufacturers' instructions) should preferably specify intervals and arrangements for inspection, and for periodic thorough examination where required. They should where appropriate indicate competence and/or qualifications required for those carrying out the work. If suitable specifications are not available from designers or manufacturers, operators should draw up their own, to be set down as part of the pool operating procedure.

63   Operators should ensure that inspections, tests and thorough examinations are undertaken at the specified intervals, and required maintenance is promptly carried out. Records should be kept of inspections etc, their results, and any remedial work carried out.

SAFE WORKING PRACTICES: GENERAL REQUIREMENTS

64   The employer's general duties towards the health and safety of employees, under the Health and Safety at Work etc Act 1974 (HSW Act), are outlined in paragraphs 4 to 6 of the Introduction to the Guidance. In more detail, employers must ensure, so far as is reasonably practicable, the health and safety of their employees in the following areas:

(a)   the workplace (including means of access and egress);

(b)   dust, fume and noise;

(c)   plant and machinery;

(d)   systems of work;

(e)   use, handling, storage and transport of articles and substances;

(f)   working conditions, including adequate lighting, heating, ventilation, toilet facilities etc; and

(g)   information, instruction, training and supervision.

65   Employers are also required to:

(a)   draw up and revise as appropriate a health and safety policy statement, if they have five or more employees, and bring it to their notice (HSE has produced guidance on how to prepare a written health and safety policy)[42,43];

(b)   consult any safety representatives appointed by recognised trades unions on health and safety matters. Safety representatives are entitled to certain information, and to paid time off to train for their role;

(c)   provide, free, any protective clothing or equipment required by law; and

(d)   provide adequate and suitable first-aid facilities for employees.

66   Employees have certain duties under the HSW Act. They must take reasonable care of their own health and safety, and that of others who may be affected by their acts or omissions at work. They must cooperate with employers in complying with statutory health and safety obligations.

Training

67 Staff should be adequately trained for the duties they will carry out.

68 The Institute of Baths and Recreation Management (IBRM) organises a number of courses relevant to the management of swimming pools, including courses for recreation supervisors, swimming pool attendants and pool plant operators. This last course deals with many of the technical aspects of pool water treatment including disinfection systems; the chemicals used; disinfection equipment; water circulation and filtration. There is a separate section dealing with safety. The swimming pool attendants course covers hygiene, in relation to pool cleaning requirements; employee safety; accident and emergency procedures; public relations; security, legal and general matters and the design and operation of swimming pools.

Safe access and safe place of work

69 Wherever employees or contractors are required to work, safe means of access, and a safe place of work, must be provided so far as is reasonably practicable*. More detailed advice for some specific work activities is given later in this chapter. In general, at swimming pools particular care - and suitable precautions - may be needed where:

(a) employees work in 'wet' areas, where surfaces may become slippery, and use of electricity poses particular risks;

(b) a warm, humid atmosphere may cause drowsiness - this may be particularly important where employees are working indoors, at heights;

(c) there is a risk of drowning from falling into an unsupervised pool, or into a water tank; or

(d) there is a risk of falling more than 2 m to the base of a pool which is empty or at reduced depth.

Protecting the public during maintenance etc activities

70 Suitable precautions should be taken to protect any of the public who may be

*See Introduction to the Guidance, paragraphs 5 - 6

present during work activities. It is recommended elsewhere (paragraphs 167-168) that effective measures should be taken to prevent unauthorised public access to a pool intended to be out of use. Particular consideration is needed where the public may have access - unauthorised, or otherwise - alongside a pool which is empty, or at a reduced depth. Management should consider who may be at risk, and consider the need for edge protection, as appropriate.

Reporting of injuries etc to enforcing authorities

71 Under the Reporting of Injuries, Diseases and Dangerous Occurrences Regulations 1985, employers must report to the relevant enforcing authority for health and safety legislation, certain injuries and dangerous occurrences affecting employees, or the public. These requirements are summarised at Appendix 3.

FIRST AID

72 Under the Health and Safety (First Aid) Regulations 1981[44], employers must make adequate first aid provision for their employees in case they are injured or become ill at work. 'Adequate' first aid provision means that which is likely to be required to cater for foreseeable types of injury or illness resulting from accidents. HSE has published further advice[45]. In particular, risks associated with chemicals (paragraphs 113 to 126) and electric shock (paragraph 107) should be taken into account.

73 The 1981 Regulations apply only to employees. Employers should however ensure that first aid provision also caters adequately for foreseeable types of accidents to pool users.

STRUCTURE AND FINISHES OF THE BUILDING AND POOL

Maintenance

74 *Floors, passages, ramps and stairs should be properly maintained and, so far as is reasonably practicable*, kept free of obstructions and of any substance likely to cause slipping.* HSE has published general guidance on the prevention of slips, trips and falls[46].

75   *Floor surfaces in 'wet' areas, where people will walk barefoot, should be carefully maintained, to avoid injury from sharp edges etc.* Sharp tile edges may become exposed, due to joint sealant losing its adhesion with them and dropping beneath the floor surface. Advice on repair or replacement of movement joint sealants should be obtained from sealant and tile manufacturers/suppliers.

76   It is also important in 'wet' areas that:

(a)   broken or missing tiles are replaced quickly;

(b)   there is no accumulation of working materials or other debris which could cause injury to bare feet; and

(c)   drainage is adequate, to avoid surfaces becoming slippery.

77   *Buildings should generally be inspected annually.* However, the high humidity levels in swimming pool buildings, possibly aggravated by chemicals in the atmosphere, may increase corrosion. This is likely to particularly affect suspended ceilings, pendant light fittings and similar structures, which may need more frequent inspection (eg every six months). Inspections should pay particular attention to roof spaces and voids, where ventilation may be poor.

Safe working practices

78   *Where frequent access is required to roofs, roof voids or other raised areas, permanent means of access should if possible be provided.* For outside roofs, this should preferably be by stairways or fixed ladders with safety hoops. There is a relevant British Standard[47]. Unauthorised access should be prevented, eg by locked doors or removable ladder sections.

79   *Where access is required infrequently, this can be provided by temporary means:* scaffolding (and staging where necessary to provide a temporary place of work) or - where this provides a sufficiently safe means - by ladders.

80   *Scaffolding should be erected and used only by those trained and competent to do so.* HSE has published guidance on

large general access scaffolds required during construction work or major alterations, and on prefabricated tower scaffolds[48,49].

81   *Ladders, step ladders and trestles should be of sound construction, properly maintained, and suitable in size and strength for the use to which they are put. They should be used only by suitably trained and competent employees.* HSE has produced guidance on the safe use of ladders etc[50]. Before a ladder is used, checks should ensure that:

(a)   the nature of the work, type of tools required and the weight of any article to be fixed do not threaten the ladder's stability;

(b)   it is securely fixed against slipping outwards or sideways;

(c)   it is not so long or so flexible that sway and vibration could cause loss of balance;

(d)   the structure against which the ladder is to rest is adequately strong and stable;

(e)   the user has a safe hand-hold and is close enough to the work; and

(f)   site conditions (eg weather, or likely movement of people or vehicles) do not pose a hazard.

82   *If employees are required to work near open edges of a roof (or if the public could gain access), and a fall of more than 2 m would be possible, suitable permanent edge protection should be provided.* Temporary edge protection may suffice if access is required only rarely. Detailed guidance is available from HSE[51]. Where construction work is undertaken, the requirements of Regulations under the Factories Act 1961[52-55] should be complied with. HSE has also published a booklet[56] which describes some accidents caused by unsafe working practices, and how they could have been avoided.

83   Whenever employees work in raised areas where they are liable to fall a distance of more than 2 m, or into water, and a ladder does not provide a safe place of work, a working platform of adequate size and strength, with suitable

edge protection, should if possible be provided. (For precautions where employees work above fragile ceilings etc see paragraph 97.)

HEATING, VENTILATION AND AIR CONDITIONING SYSTEMS

Maintenance

84   *Heating plant and associated fuel storage and delivery systems should be regularly inspected and tested, and properly maintained, in line with manufacturers' instructions, and British Standards where relevant*[57-73].

85   *Steam boilers and plant should be maintained to the standards required by Section 32-35 of the Factories Act 1961.* This includes a requirement for regular, thorough examination by a competent person. The boiler should be examined after dismantling when cold, and also examined while operating under normal conditions. After any substantial repair, the boiler should be re-examined. After each examination, a certificate should be obtained, and kept available for inspection.

86   *Where bunded fuel storage tanks are sited in the open air, rainwater collected in the bund should preferably be pumped out over the bund walls.* Where bunds have drain valves, operators should ensure they are kept closed, unless being used.

87   *Storage vessels and delivery pipeline systems for liquefied petroleum gas (LPG) should be installed and maintained in accordance with HSE Booklet HS(G) 34*[16].

88   *Ventilation systems should be inspected regularly (eg every three months) and adequately maintained, including cleaning of filter units.* The system's effectiveness should be monitored at least annually. It is helpful to record how dampers have been adjusted, together with air flow rates and static pressure readings, so that the system can be maintained to the original standard. For further information and advice see references 10 and 19-23.

Safe working practices

89   *Any manufacturers' instructions on how to operate boilers and associated plant safely should be made conveniently available to attendants (eg by attaching* copies to the plant itself). Instructions and training should cover both normal operating conditions, and action necessary in the event of an emergency or breakdown.

90   *Where pipework associated with boilers and similar plant will become hot enough to cause injury, it should be adequately lagged.*

91   *Suitable precautions should be taken where employees must enter confined spaces for maintenance or other work.* The advice in paragraph 157 should be followed (insofar as it is relevant), and reference made to HSE guidance on working in confined spaces[74].

92   *Asbestos was widely used in the past for insulation and fire protection, and may be found in swimming pool premises, especially in lagging for heating systems etc.* A DoE publication[75] gives guidance on the common types of asbestos materials and where they may be found in buildings.

93   All work with asbestos is now subject to the Control of Asbestos at Work Regulations 1987[76]. Associated with the regulations are two Approved Codes of Practice; one dealing with general work, and a special Code for work with asbestos insulation, asbestos coatings and asbestos insulation board[77,78]. Any pool operator whose employees may work with asbestos must prepare a risk assessment (normally in writing). This should identify the types of asbestos, determine the nature and degree of exposure, and set out the steps to be taken to prevent or reduce exposure to the lowest reasonably practicable level.

94   Most of the work with asbestos insulation and coatings can only be carried out by persons licensed by HSE under the Asbestos (Licensing) Regulations 1983[79]. This work has to be done in accordance with the Regulations and Codes mentioned in the previous paragraph. It is unlikely that most pool operators will have the necessary expertise or equipment, or adequately trained staff; in general such work should be done by competent, licensed contractors. Pool operators should satisfy themselves that contractors are working in accordance with the Codes, and

preventing the spread of asbestos dust from the working area.

LIGHTING

Maintenance

95   A good standard of illumination is important to safety (see paragraphs 46-49). To ensure that this is maintained:

(a)   external windows should be kept clean;

(b)   artificial lighting should be maintained in good working order, with units kept clean (where appropriate), and promptly replaced if defective; and

(c)   any emergency lighting should be tested daily.

Safe working practices

96   Access for window cleaning poses some special problems, additional to the general ones (see above) connected with working at heights. HSE has published guidance[80].

97   Where work is required above fragile ceilings, roofs or rooflights, suitable walkways and platforms should be provided. These should:

(a)   be of adequate dimensions and strength, and properly supported;

(b)   have suitable edge protection (toe boards, hand-rails and mid-rails) as required; and

(c)   take the employee close enough to the work to avoid any risk of overbalancing.

HSE general guidance on edge protection etc[51] is relevant.

98   Tools or other articles used at heights should be secured/tethered wherever possible. Employees should take care not to drop articles through fragile materials onto people below.

ELECTRICAL INSTALLATIONS AND EQUIPMENT

Maintenance

99   *Fixed electrical installations should be inspected and tested to the standards in the current edition of 'Regulations for Electrical Installations', published by the Institution of Electrical Engineers[30]. Because of the wet and corrosive conditions, inspections and tests should be done at least annually, and more frequently for equipment subject to more arduous conditions (eg high humidity).*

100   *Any equipment for use in areas with potentially explosive atmospheres should be maintained in accordance with British Standard 5345 Part 1[39], and any guidance given by the manufacturer.*

101   *Transportable and portable equipment should be inspected and tested at 3, 6 or 12-monthly intervals, depending on the use to which it is put.* Testing should ensure the efficiency and effectiveness of any protective conductor, the insulation resistance of flexible leads, plugs and that of the equipment, the correct fusing of the device and correct polarity of electrical connections. Records should be kept of the dates and results of tests and of any remedial work carried out.

102   *Residual Current Circuit-Breakers (RCCBs) should be tested regularly by operating the test button, before the equipment to which they are connected is operated.* They should normally be tested at least daily or, if used less than once a day, every time they are used.

103   *Pool operators should have an effective system for ensuring that faulty equipment is reported to management, and immediately withdrawn from use until repaired by a competent person.*

Safe working practices

104   *Work on electrical installations and equipment requires specialist skills.* It should only be performed by employees who are suitably trained and competent, in relation to the equipment and the work in question.

105   Conductors which are potentially dangerous when live should be made dead and isolated from the supply before any work is done on or near them, to prevent inadvertent reconnection to the system while work is in progress. This can be done for example by removing the fuses which control the system, or by opening the switch and locking the

'locking-off' facility which is fitted to some switchgear.

106   Access to necessarily live, exposed conductors at voltages not exceeding 650 V (eg a boiler control panel which has been opened) must be restricted to those who are trained and competent to recognise their dangers. A second person should always be present. (Conductors at higher voltages should be behind locked doors - see paragraph 54 of the previous chapter.)

107   Staff likely to be responsible for electrical equipment should be trained in giving treatment for electric shock. It is useful to display the names of staff with such training, next to main switchboards, in plant rooms, and at any other relevant locations.

Swimming is a family activity

THE POOL WATER
TREATMENT SYSTEM

THE POOL WATER TREATMENT SYSTEM

INTRODUCTION

108 This chapter gives guidance on how systems for the disinfection, filtration and circulation of pool water (including arrangements for the storage and handling of chemicals) should be operated to ensure the safety of employees and pool users. It does not cover standards of water quality, the effectiveness of disinfection systems, or related matters such as water testing. The Department of the Environment (DoE) has published general guidance on these matters[81,82] and specific guidance on the efficiency of commonly used disinfection systems[83-86].

109 The main hazards associated with pool water treatment systems include:

(a) *risks to bathers from unclear water.* As well as indicating that water treatment and quality is inadequate, unclear water is a safety hazard: (see paragraph 162);

(b) *risks to employees or bathers from chemicals used in disinfection systems.* These include irritation of skin or eyes; enhanced flammability of materials due to disinfectants being strong oxidising agents; and leaks of toxic gases. The most serious risk is of an uncontrolled escape of chlorine gas, eg following inadvertent mixing of chlorine-based disinfectant with acids;

(c) *miscellaneous risks to employees,* from work in confined spaces, use of electrical equipment etc.

SAFE WORKING PRACTICES: GENERAL REQUIREMENTS

110 Many of the systems and processes described in this chapter involve potentially dangerous chemicals. The written safety policy should include management's assessment of hazards associated with all aspects of operation of the plant, and precautions to control the risks.

111 Adequate training should be provided, and records kept. Training should:

(a) be related specifically to the operation of the particular plant, hazards associated with it, and substances used. Employees' attention should be drawn to any manufacturers' instructions, and copies made conveniently available (for example, secured to the plant itself);

(b) be given to enough employees to ensure that plant need never be operated by untrained staff;

(c) include line management, to ensure they understand the plant and associated hazards sufficiently to supervise safe operation;

(d) include the use, care and maintenance of personal protective equipment;

(e) require those who have been trained to demonstrate that they can operate and maintain the plant safely.

112 For training courses provided by the Institute of Baths and Recreation Management, see paragraph 68.

DELIVERY, STORAGE AND HANDLING OF CHEMICALS

113 Advice on delivery, storage and handling of chemicals is given in a series of DoE booklets[87-91]. These include advice for small systems using small quantities of materials.

Delivery to site

114 When chemicals are to be delivered, sufficient space for parking and manoeuvring should be provided close to the storage area. Precautions (eg supervision, warning signs, or barriers) should be taken as necessary to protect the public or employees who may have access to the delivery area. Materials should be moved into storage as soon as possible, and never left unattended in a public area.

115 For bulk deliveries a written delivery procedure should be agreed with the supplier. Incompatible materials (eg acid and alkali) if delivered in the same vehicle, should be effectively segregated. Where more than one chemical is delivered in bulk, pipework should be of

different types, or fitting sizes, to prevent delivery hoses being incorrectly connected up. Loading points should be clearly labelled.

116   Cylinders and drums should be clearly labelled with their contents. Packaging and labelling should comply with the Classification, Packaging and Labelling of Dangerous Substances Regulations 1984[92].

117   Suitably designed trolleys or similar equipment should be used to transport cylinders and heavy drums, which should be kept upright. Liquid bromine containers require particularly careful handling (see paragraph 123).

Storage

118   Storage rooms and areas should:

(a)   be clearly marked, and in secure locations accessible only by authorised employees. If materials are stored in plant rooms, a defined area should be set aside for them;

(b)   preferably be on the ground floor, and accessed directly from outside. This will assist ventilation, and movement of materials (including in an emergency);

(c)   not be sited close to public entrances, windows or ventilation intakes. This reduces the risk of any release of toxic fumes being drawn into the building;

(d)   have adequate natural ventilation to the open air in a safe position (ie not to a public area, or to a place from where fumes may enter the building). If adequate natural ventilation is not reasonably practicable*, mechanical ventilation should be provided. Where failure of ventilation would pose a serious hazard (eg for a chlorine store), a flow switch should be incorporated in any mechanical system, to sound an alarm in the event of fan breakdown;

(e)   preferably also provide fire-resistant enclosures for non-flammable chemicals, in view of other risks from over-heating, such as:

(i)   dangerous fumes being given off;

(ii)   leakage from damaged plastic containers;

(iii)   explosion of pressurised containers.

Containers should not be stored in direct sunlight, or next to hot pipework or plant;

(f)   provide clean and dry storage for solid materials (which may need to be raised off the ground if areas will be hosed down or flooding is possible).

119   Different chemicals should be effectively segregated, in storage and use. This is particularly important for sodium hypochlorite and hydrochloric acid, which react together to produce chlorine gas. Further advice on the safe storage of particular chemicals and gases is in paragraphs 145 and 153 below.

120   Where liquids are stored in bulk fixed tanks, including day tanks, bunding capable of holding 110% of the largest container within the bund should be provided. Similar bunding should be provided for portable containers, where reasonably practicable*.

Handling of chemicals

121   Safe systems of work should be followed to protect employees from contacting, ingesting or inhaling harmful materials. *When handling dry materials, employees should not be exposed to excessive dust.* Where necessary, conditions for weighing out materials etc should be carefully controlled. Suitable scoops etc should be provided to discourage manual handling. Exhaust ventilation may need to be considered.

122   Depending on the type of disinfection system, some or all of the following *protective clothing* may be needed during delivery, handling of materials, cleaning or maintenance:

(a)   impervious boots;

(b)   impervious aprons;

(c)   impervious gauntlets; and

(d)   eye protection to the relevant British Standard[93].

*See Introduction to the Guidance, paragraphs 5-6

'Impervious' means in relation to chemicals likely to be encountered: for further advice see reference 94.

123   With systems using chlorine or liquid bromine, normal plant operation implies a risk of exposure to toxic gases (eg during changeover of chlorine or liquid bromine containers). Suitable *respiratory protection* should be provided for employees, who should be trained in its use.

124   A British Standard[95] describes the main types of respiratory equipment available, and their suitability for particular purposes. The equipment most commonly used for protection against anticipated minor leakages is the canister respirator. A further British Standard[96] gives information about canisters and cartridges suitable for particular toxic hazards.

125   Where canister respirators are to be used, it is important that:

(a)   a respirator should be sited immediately outside the plant room, with a further respirator near to hand at any point where a leak can be anticipated. Minor leaks should preferably be dealt with by two employees; an additional respirator should be provided for this. Adequate and clean accommodation should be provided for respirators;

(b)   a good seal between the respirator and the user's face should be ensured. Training is necessary to achieve a good fit. The seal should be tested (for recommended methods, see references 95-96);

(c)   unless on personal issue, respirators should be disinfected after use; and

(d)   canisters should be replaced when they have been used for the maximum period recommended by the manufacturer. Usage therefore needs to be recorded. An inspection and maintenance contract is helpful.

126   Canister respirators are unsuitable for use in concentrations of gas over 1% by volume. Pool operators need to consider suitable emergency procedures for more serious leaks, in consultation with the fire authorities where

appropriate. Should employees be required to deal with such incidents, they will need appropriate breathing apparatus and training. Unless these are provided, employees should be instructed that, if they have difficulty breathing or there are any other indications of excess concentrations of gas, they should leave the room immediately and seek assistance.

FIRST AID

127   First aid provision (see paragraphs 72-73) should be adequate to deal with the consequences of chemical splashes, for example, onto the skin or into the eyes.

SPILLAGES; DISPOSAL OF WASTES; MAJOR LEAK OF TOXIC GASES

128   Any spillages should be quickly cleared away using a safe method. Care should be taken to prevent any chemical from entering a drain, unless with the prior agreement of the Water Authority.

Disposal of wastes

129   The manufacturer's instructions concerning disposal of containers and materials should be followed. Where chemical wastes are to be removed from premises, the Waste Disposal Authority should be consulted.

Major leak of toxic gases

130   There should be a written emergency procedure for dealing with any major, uncontrolled release of toxic gas. The procedure should include arrangements for:

(a)   evacuating the whole site, if necessary; and

(b)   coordination with the emergency services, including informing them immediately of hazardous substances present (unless they already have this information).

131   In certain exceptional circumstances (for example, where more than 10 tonnes of chlorine are stored) the premises may be subject to the Notification of Installations Handling Hazardous Substances Regulations 1982[97], or the Control of Industrial Major Accident Hazards Regulations 1984[98]. The local

HSE area office should be consulted, as necessary.

HAZARDS ASSOCIATED WITH PARTICULAR DISINFECTION SYSTEMS

132   Advice on the safe design and operation of the most commonly-used disinfection systems is given in a series of booklets published by DoE[87-90]. Some important considerations are discussed below.

Sodium hypochlorite and acid systems

133   Pool water treatment systems which dose the pool water automatically with sodium hypochlorite and acid have resulted in the release of chlorine gas into the atmosphere. Numerous incidents have occurred when water circulation has stopped, or been reduced, but the automatic dosing system has continued to operate. This produces a build-up of sodium hypochlorite and acid, which react together to produce chlorine gas: the gas is then discharged when water circulation is restored.

134   The loss of water circulation or reduced flow can be caused by failure of the pumps; loss of prime; manual isolation of the pumps during maintenance; or the operation of by-pass valves (which reduce water flow within the pipeline).

135   In all disinfection systems which incorporate automatic chemical dosing, the following precautions should be considered, as appropriate:

(a)   interlocking the dosing system with the water circulating pumps, to prevent the continuation of dosing should the pumps fail;

(b)   incorporating into the circulation system a flow switch capable of detecting a reduction or cessation of flow. The design should be 'fail-safe' (see paragraphs 150-151);

(c)   siting the pool water circulation pumps below the level of the pool water, to minimise the risk of the pumps losing their prime;

(d)   locating an additional sampling point close to the chemical injection point for alarm purposes. (Automatic dosing systems operate by sampling the water and activating or stopping the dosing pumps as required, for example following a change in bather loads. An additional sampling point near the injection point should ensure that in the event of an excessive build-up of chemicals, dosing ceases automatically. The equipment supplier should be consulted before an installation is modified);

(e)   siting the sodium hypochlorite and acid injection points as far apart as possible;

(f)   displaying notices warning of the risks of mixing sodium hypochlorite and acids, and the importance of maintaining pool water circulation during dosing;

(g)   ensuring that pipelines containing sodium hypochlorite and acid are drained and flushed out before maintenance work is carried out.

Electrolytic generation of sodium hypochlorite

136   Hazards stem from the production of flammable hydrogen and, occasionally, the generation of chlorine gas.

137   Hydrogen gas released during the electrolytic process should be vented safely into the open air. Selection and siting of any electrical equipment associated with the electrolytic generator requires careful consideration. (See other chapters for detailed advice on the design, selection and maintenance of electrical equipment.)

138   Maintenance of electrical equipment is likely to be a job for specialist staff, but plant operators should be aware of the general hazards of using electrical equipment in these processes.

139   Suitable protective clothing for handling hypochlorite, acid etc should be provided where necessary, together with respiratory equipment for use in an emergency (eg the generation of excessive levels of chlorine).

Ozone systems

140   Guidance on the design, installation, operation and maintenance of ozone systems is given in a British Effluent and Water Association Code of Practice[99].

A national survey of ozone water treatment systems for swimming pools has been published by the Sports Council[100]. Hazards can arise from the chemicals used (ozone, hypochlorite, acid) and from the electrical ozone generating process.

141 Additional guidance on health hazards associated with ozone has been published by HSE[101]. It is strongly recommended that ozonators are automatically shut down in any of the following abnormal operating conditions:

(a) air drier failure;

(b) cooling water failure;

(c) loss of vacuum (or excess pressure, depending on the system);

(d) circulation pump failure;

(e) excess or low electrical power;

(f) air flow failure.

It is also recommended that the monitoring of ozone in the atmosphere ensures automatic ozonator shut down at 0.3 ppm ozone or less, whilst activating warning alarms at 0.1 ppm or less.

142 Ozone devices have sometimes been installed to remove ambient odours, eg in changing rooms. Ozone levels from such systems must not be allowed to exceed the recommended occupational health limit set out in HSE Guidance Note EH 40[102].

Chlorine gas systems

143 Chlorine can be a particular hazard. Government advisory circulars issued in 1978/79[103] recommended that its use as a pool disinfectant should cease by 1 January 1985. However, where chlorine systems are still in operation, account should be taken of the information in the following two paragraphs.

144 HSE guidance[104] on using chlorine from drums and cylinders and DoE guidance on chlorine gas disinfection systems[87] should be carefully followed. Particular care should be taken when changing cylinders.

145 It is important that:

(a) associated pipework is made of suitable material, adequately supported, and clearly labelled;

(b) full and empty cylinders are clearly identified, and secured so they cannot fall over. Storage should be away from working areas, in well ventilated, secure locations;

(c) employees are adequately trained in the handling and use of chlorine in cylinders;

(d) suitable personal protective equipment (including respiratory protection) is provided; and

(e) there is a written emergency procedure.

See HSE guidance[104] for further, detailed advice.

Elemental liquid bromine systems

146 Though less hazardous than pressurised liquid gas systems such as chlorine, elemental liquid bromine too requires careful handling. The main risks are of spillage of either liquid bromine itself, or of bromine water. Containers should be used and stored within a bunded area; and should be handled gently, to avoid damage to the fragile inner container.

147 Adequate supplies of neutralizing materials, such as sodium carbonate or sodium thiosulphate solutions, should be available near to hand, and there should be ready access to emergency shower facilities.

Calcium hypochlorite, chloroisocyanurate, halogenated dimethylhydantoin and solid ancillary chemical systems

148 The hazards associated with these materials are largely those of chemical handling generally. There is also a risk of chlorine gas being generated if chemicals come into contact with acids, or from contact between dry chemicals and water.

149 It is important that:

(a) dry chemicals are not added to the pool while bathers are using it, nor should bathers be readmitted until all materials have fully dissolved and dispersed;

(b) employees have adequate personal

protective equipment (including respiratory equipment, where there is a risk of exposure to chlorine);

(c) the plant room is adequately ventilated;

(d) any associated pipework and valves are adequately labelled and supported; and

(e) there is no risk of water coming into contact with the chemicals when the system is shut down.

Fail-safe systems

150 Some systems have been designed to 'fail-safe' to prevent releases of chlorine gas. Such systems may operate by providing a water supply from the delivery side of the pool water circulation pump, passing it through the feeder device and returning the disinfectant solution to the suction side of the pump. Such devices need a continuous flow of water through them - see DoE guidance[91] for design and operation of systems using calcium hypochlorite, chloroisocyanurates, halogenated dimethylhydantoins and solid ancillary chemicals. Electrical failure of the circulating pump motor, or loss of prime, will stop the admission of disinfection to the circulating system, but care may be needed on re-starting.

151 Chemical dosing pumps operated by water pressure and regulated by a mechanical water meter also offer a 'fail-safe' system.

The use of carbon dioxide for pH adjustment

152 The use of carbon dioxide for pH adjustment is becoming more common. The system works by metering carbon dioxide gas into the water recirculation system. It has the advantage that, unlike hypochlorite and acid systems, there is no possibility of the accidental generation of chlorine gas.

153 Bulk storage of liquid carbon dioxide (particularly in a relatively confined space) does however carry its own risks: displacement of oxygen, leading to asphyxiation; and toxicity at high concentrations. Bulk CO_2 should be stored outside buildings in well-ventilated

*See Introduction to the Guidance, paragraphs 5-6

areas. HSE has produced guidance[105].

SAND FILTERS: CLEANING AND MAINTENANCE

154 Sand filters are commonly used in large pools. They require regular back-washing to remove material caught in the filter medium. Adequate disinfection of the filter medium should be maintained.

155 Back-washing will tend to lower the level of water in the pool. If it is to be carried out when the pool is in use, suitable precautions should be taken to protect bathers. (Reduced depth may be dangerous to divers. This can be avoided by increasing the water level, before back-washing; but it may then be necessary to warn users, particularly non-swimmers, of the increased depth.)

156 In multiple filter installations, back-washing should be staggered. This makes it easier to control the pool water level, and reduces the risk that the disinfectant residual will fall below the recommended minimum concentration. Automatic make-up and levelling devices can help maintain the correct water level, especially when back-washing is carried out frequently (eg daily).

157 Cleaning or maintenance activities may require employees to enter filter vessels. Advice published by HSE on working in confined spaces[74] should be carefully followed. In particular:

(a) there should be safe access and egress. Rectangular or oval manholes should, so far as is reasonably practicable*, be not less than 46 cm (18 inches) long, and 41 cm (16 inches) wide. Circular manholes should be not less than 46 cm (18 inches) in diameter. On new plant, manholes should always be provided to at least this standard. Another person (suitably trained) and suitable rescue equipment should be on hand whenever a person is working in a confined space;

(b) before entering the space, tests should be carried out as appropriate to check on the presence of gas, fumes or chemical deposits. Employees should not be exposed to toxic fumes above the limits recommended in the most recent

29

edition of HSE Guidance Note EH 40[102]; or to excessive dust. The adequacy of the oxygen supply (whether through natural, or artificial, ventilation) needs to be checked. The space should be certified as safe for entry without personal respiratory equipment (or alternatively, this should be provided);

(c)   where flammable vapours will be generated, these should be diluted sufficiently to avoid a concentration exceeding 25% of the lower flammable limit of the material. All potential sources of ignition should be excluded from the vessel. Particular attention should be given to any electrical equipment: only suitable explosion-protected electrical equipment should be used in potentially flammable atmospheres. See guidance published by HSE[41].

A class in operation in a deck level pool and a public session in adjacent pool with a lifeguard on duty

SUPERVISION ARRANGEMENTS TO SAFEGUARD POOL USERS

SUPERVISION ARRANGEMENTS TO SAFEGUARD POOL USERS

INTRODUCTION

158   All pools require some measure of supervision, to promote safety when in use.

159   Detailed arrangements need to be considered by the pool operator, taking account of all local circumstances: the pool structure, equipment, manner of use, and characteristics of those who may use the pool.

160   The large variety of possible settings is indicated below:

(a)   most pools are rectangular (the 'tank' type), but many newer ones are irregular, both in shape and depth (the 'leisure' or 'beach' concept);

(b)   pools vary considerably in depth, and in the types of equipment (if any) provided. They may be provided indoors, or outdoors;

(c)   pools may be used for general swimming or for 'programmed' swimming (where use is 'disciplined', as for lessons, competitive training etc). Or they may (as with many leisure pools) not be used for swimming at all, but for play and relaxation;

(d)   while, in the past, many pools have been run by local authorities for general public use, pools are now increasingly being incorporated in other types of premises (such as holiday camps, hotels or hospitals) with limited or no general public access.

161   Against this background, published general guidelines can do no more than provide a starting point. Arrangements at any given pool may also need to be varied from time to time, according to current use.

ASPECTS OF SUPERVISION RELEVANT TO ALL POOLS

Awareness of risks

162   The starting point for planning safe procedures must be an appreciation of the main hazards and users at risk. The following have been factors in past fatalities (or serious injuries):

(a)   prior health problems (heart trouble, asthma etc);

(b)   alcohol or food before swimming;

(c)   youth and inexperience (half of those who drown are aged under 15);

(d)   weak or non-swimmers straying out of their depth;

(e)   unauthorised access to pools intended to be out of use;

(f)   diving into insufficient depth of water (leading to concussion, or injury to head or spine);

(g)   unruly behaviour and misuse of equipment;

(h)   unclear pool water, preventing casualties from being seen;

(i)   absence of, or inadequate response by, lifeguards in an emergency.

Careful recording and consideration of any incidents experienced at the pool will help managers ensure that safety arrangements remain relevant. It is useful to draw attention to any particular risk factors, in the pool operating procedures. (Certain kinds of incident must be reported to the enforcing authorities for health and safety legislation: see paragraph 71 and Appendix 3.)

Encouraging responsible behaviour by bathers

163   Any pool will be safer if bathers are aware of potential hazards, and act responsibly. Appendix 4 contains a suggested Swimming Pool Users' Safety Code, which may be a helpful starting point for managers, in reminding pool users of key safety points. Ways of drawing them to bathers' attention could include, for example:

(a)   notices displayed at reception, in changing areas or on the poolside;

(b)   a leaflet handed to bathers as they arrive, and to those in charge of organised groups (including school parties);

(c)   references in contracts with club organisers, schools etc hiring the pool;

(d)   oral reminders, where necessary, by lifeguards.

(A poster based on the Code has been prepared by RoSPA, with the support of HSE, the Sports Council, and the Royal Life Saving Society, and is obtainable from RoSPA; see Appendix 7 for address.)

Written operating procedures

164   It is recommended that every pool operator should prepare a written operating procedure setting out the organisation and arrangements for ensuring users' safety. This will be for reference both by the pool's own staff, and by club organisers and others who may use the pool. The length and complexity of the written procedure will vary greatly, according to the circumstances of the particular pool; but it should include both a normal operating plan and an emergency action plan. A checklist, which may provide a useful starting point, is at Appendix 5. (More detailed advice on particular aspects is given below.) The written procedure should be updated regularly, as required.

165   Where the pool is an ancillary part of a larger complex (eg a hotel, hospital or school), a senior member of management should be clearly designated as responsible for safe pool operation.

Staff training

166   Staff who will be concerned in any way with supervising access to, or use of, the pool, need adequate training. They should:

(a)   know and understand pool operating procedures, so far as their role may require; and

(b)   understand the safety aspects of their own duties and be fully competent to deal with these.

(For detailed recommendations on lifeguards' training, see paragraphs 189-197 below.)

Controlling access to the pool

167   *Preventing unauthorised access.* Effective measures (physical barriers, supervision, or both) should be taken to prevent unauthorised access to a pool intended to be out of use.

168   *Pool covers.* Various types of pool cover are available, including simple hand-operated roller systems, automatically deployed covers, rising floors and decks and air-supported domes. The Sports Council has published information about them[106]. Where pool covers are used as the primary means of preventing bathers' access (for example, in some open air pools, which cannot be locked off after hours), the covers must be of a type which can be secured continuously around the edges. They must be capable of supporting the weight of any person walking or falling onto them.

169   *Controlling maximum admissions.* Pool operators should assess the maximum numbers that can safely be admitted to the pool. Should there be a risk of the number being exceeded, admissions should be restricted.

170   The Department of the Environment has recommended that a minimum water area of 2 m^2 per bather be allowed for physical safety[82]. Managers should not, however, follow this figure slavishly, but should assess what is a maximum safe density in the particular circumstances of their pool and its current use. For example:

(a)   a higher density may be reasonable in a pool with a large area of shallow water;

(b)   a lower density may be appropriate where significant space must be allowed for activities such as poolside diving, or use of water slides.

171   Since admissions will in practice be controlled at the point of entry to the pool complex rather than to the water itself, allowance can be made, in setting a maximum figure, for the proportion of bathers likely to be out of the water (eg for changing, or poolside activities) at any given time. At leisure pools this may be a significant proportion. At the same time allowance should be made for any sudden large influxes of bathers to the water which can reasonably be expected (particularly associated with the operation of wave machines).

172   Managers should set the appropriate maximum limit for their pool following due observation, over a period,

of typical bather behaviour. As well as considerations of physical safety, the maximum loading should take account of the capacity of the pool water treatment system: see paragraph 109 and advice published by DoE[82]. The maximum figure should be set out in the written operating procedures.

Water clarity

173   As well as indicating that water quality is inadequate (see the previous chapter), unclear water is a safety hazard. It makes it more difficult (for example) for a diver entering the water to see swimmers below the surface; or for a casualty to be spotted. The clarity of the pool water should be constantly monitored. Should it begin to deteriorate, the pool should be cleared or admissions suspended until a satisfactory standard is reached.

Emergency equipment and alarm systems

174   Equipment provided for emergency use should be kept in its proper place, and maintained in good working order.

175   A poolside alarm for summoning outside help is recommended. Alarms should be tested daily.

Hire to outside organisations

176   The legal responsibilities of employers and those in charge of premises towards the safety of those (other than employees) using their premises, are outlined in the Introduction to the Guidance (paragraphs 4-6). These need to be borne in mind when considering with outside hirers arrangements for safety during their sessions. The arrangements should be agreed in advance, and set out in writing. Appendix 6 sets out a check-list of points for inclusion in hire contracts

177   Where lifeguards are required, the general recommendations on duties, training and numbers, later in this chapter, should be followed as appropriate. Where agreement is reached that the group will provide for its own supervision, pool operators need to consider what, if any, additional cover they need provide, bearing in mind that:

(a)   they retain residual responsibilities for the safety of all who use the pool and its facilities;

Leisure pool with beach area and slide discharging into its own landing pool

(b) where the hire group shares use of the pool with the general public, the pool operator remains solely responsible for ensuring the latter's safety; and

(c) it will usually in practice be necessary for the pool operator to have a responsible person on the premises.

178   Pool operators should take reasonable steps to assure themselves that arrangements for safety, agreed with hirers, are implemented. It is reasonable for example to check from time to time that agreed supervision is being carried out, and any agreed rules of behaviour observed; or to ask for documentary evidence of lifeguards' competence.

PRECAUTIONS WHERE CONSTANT POOLSIDE SUPERVISION IS NOT PROVIDED

Factors to be considered in deciding whether constant poolside supervision is necessary

179   Constant poolside supervision by lifeguards provides the best assurance of pool users' safety. It is recognised that there are some cases where constant supervision will not be 'reasonably practicable'*. Before deciding this, pool operators should carefully consider all relevant circumstances: the nature of the pool, pool users, and activities in the pool at any particular time.

180   Generally speaking, constant poolside supervision is less likely to be essential where *all* the following conditions are met:

(a) the pool is relatively small and used by limited numbers at any one time; *and*

(b) the nature of the relationship between pool management (or activity organiser), and the pool user, make it practicable to enforce 'house rules' for safe behaviour by pool users, and ensure that these are followed. Examples are the various types of private facility mentioned in paragraph 160(d) provided access is suitably restricted, eg to hotel

*See Introduction to the Guidance, paragraphs 5-6

Ramp and wide step access to a teaching pool

residents and their guests, or hospital patients and staff; and certain conditions of swimming club use; *and*

(c) there is no diving or other poolside equipment, or other features, posing particular risks.

181 Whether constant poolside supervision is required also depends on how a pool is used at any given time. For example, a pool which would not normally require poolside supervision, may need to arrange this on occasions when:

(a) the pool will be used by unaccompanied children (aged under 15);

(b) exceptionally crowded conditions are expected;

(c) food or alcohol will be available to pool users; or

(d) activities (such as disco-swimming) take place which can lead to additional risks through the high excitement generated.

On the other hand, a pool which normally has lifeguards present, may *not* need them when hired by a club whose members are all strong swimmers, and some of whom can be expected to have lifesaving skills. (The general advice on hire to outside organisations, in paragraphs 176-178 and Appendix 6, should be followed as appropriate.)

Precautions where constant poolside supervision is not provided

182 *General safety procedures.* A clear written safety procedure is particularly important where a pool may be used without constant poolside supervision. The advice in paragraphs 164-165 and Appendix 5 should be followed as appropriate.

183 *Controlling access.* In addition to the general recommendations for controlling access (paragraphs 167-168), it is important that intended restrictions on use are enforced. Where lone bathing is permitted, it is advisable to control entering and leaving so that management know who is using the pool at any given time.

184 *Emergency arrangements.* It is strongly recommended that these should include:

(a) a poolside alarm or telephone, to summon help in an emergency;

(b) suitable rescue equipment (poles, lifebelts) available by the poolside, and clearly identifiable;

(c) a notice displayed telling bathers how to summon help in an emergency.

185 Whenever the pool is in use, a member of staff should be designated as 'on call' to deal with any emergency. It is advisable that such staff be trained in rescue, resuscitation and first aid.

REQUIREMENTS FOR AN EFFECTIVE LIFEGUARD SERVICE

186 Where constant poolside supervision is required, lifeguards should be sufficient in number, adequately trained, and effectively organised and supervised.

The lifeguard's duties

187 The key tasks of the lifeguard on the poolside are to:

(a) maintain concentrated observation of the pool and pool users in order to anticipate problems (eg rowdy behaviour, or someone swimming into the path of a diver) and to identify any emergency quickly. Some bathers in difficulty may shout and splash; others may give little indication of a problem, but simply sink below the water. Both types of behaviour may be found during normal activity: concentrated vigilance is needed to detect the genuine emergency;

(b) supervise diving or other pool equipment when allocated to these duties;

(c) carry out rescues, and initiate other emergency action, as and when necessary;

(d) give immediate first aid, in the event of injury to a bather, or other emergency;

(e) communicate with bathers (and with any other lifeguards on duty) to fulfil the above tasks.

188 Lifeguards must not only be physically fit (including good vision and hearing) but mentally alert, sensible and self-disciplined. The necessary commitment can be fostered by effective leadership and example by management and supervisors. Lifeguards can be encouraged, too, to take a broad view of their duties: for example, by undertaking ancillary duties such as checking and maintaining safety and rescue equipment, and reporting incidents which may require improved safety arrangements (but see also paragraph 202(a)).

Lifeguard training

189 Knowledge and skills required depend on the circumstances of the particular pool, notably:

(a) the depth of the water;

(b) whether there are features or equipment requiring supervision; and

(c) whether a lifeguard is also required to be a qualified first-aider (see paragraph 191(d)).

190 *All* lifeguards need thorough *knowledge* of the pool's normal operating and emergency action procedures, and potential risk factors.

191 *All* lifeguards need the *skills* to:

(a) work effectively as a member of the lifeguarding team;

(b) observe the water, and effect a prompt rescue. This requires an ability to use any emergency equipment provided for this purpose, enter the water safely, swim, dive to the deepest part of the pool, recover and land a bather in difficulty;

(c) give effective resuscitation by expired air resuscitation (EAR) and by cardio-pulmonary resuscitation (CPR). If any resuscitation equipment is provided, the lifeguard should have the additional skills needed for its use;

(d) give emergency first aid. Where fully trained first-aiders are to be employed, it may be more practicable for persons other than lifeguards to

be given this training, since lifeguards would otherwise need to be released at short notice from supervision duties. Lifeguards do however need the basic first aid training to recognise serious injury (eg bleeding, possible fractures, unconsciousness and shock) and to give immediate care until further assistance arrives.

192 It is strongly recommended that a lifeguard should hold a current qualification from an appropriate training organisation. Training relevant to the knowledge and skills listed in paragraphs 190-191 is provided by the organisations listed in Appendix 7. Some courses may not meet all requirements at any given pool, and would require supplementary training.

193 *Procedures for qualification* should preferably include:

(a) independent examination;

(b) a test in water safety knowledge and pool emergency practices;

(c) a test related to the application of the normal operating procedures and emergency action procedures and equipment in the pool;

(d) a practical test of rescue skills; and

(e) a practical test, using a recognised mannikin, of cardiac pulmonary resuscitation (CPR);

(f) tests and questions on immediate first aid.

194 Supervising specialised activities may require specialised training. Appendix 7 lists some organisations who can advise on these.

195 Where pool management decides to organise its own training rather than use an outside organisation, this should cover as appropriate all the items in paragraphs 190-191.

196 Some training organisations specify a maximum period after which requalification must be obtained. Quite apart from this (and whether or not a

training organisation is used), practical rescue skills which would otherwise be used only in an emergency (such as resuscitation, or recovering a casualty from the water) should be practised frequently. Records should be kept for each lifeguard showing initial and refresher training given and qualifications held.

197 Staff may not be fully trained when first recruited. Their duties should be suitably restricted and supervised until the necessary training, and experience, are acquired.

Clothing etc

198 Lifeguards should wear distinctive clothing or other identification, for easy recognition in an emergency. They should carry whistles.

Duty spells, and structuring of duties

199 Pool management should ensure that lifeguards are properly supervised, are clear as to their duties and areas of work, and know who is in charge at any time.

200 The length and structuring of duty spells require careful consideration by pool operators; details should be set down in the written procedures. References to duty periods should normally include the maximum period of uninterrupted supervision, the length of the working day, and breaks from duty.

201 Lifeguarding requires high levels of vigilance and concentration. To be effective, continuous supervision should be maintained. There is however no medical evidence as to the maximum period for which a high vigilance level is sustainable in typical poolside conditions. When deciding the length of duty spells, managers should make due allowance for any of the following factors which are present, and which would tend to affect adversely lifeguards' concentration:

(a) poor design, affecting vision, hearing or concentration. Examples are inadequate illumination or acoustics, and excess humidity (see paragraphs 20, 21, 44 and 46-48);

(b) crowded conditions, which will tend to increase risks and noise. This

needs to be taken into account both where pools are regularly used close to capacity (see paragraphs 169-172), and where seasonal or other peak loadings are reasonably foreseeable;

(c) distractions from poolside activities, eg radios, ball games etc in outdoor pools;

202 The structuring of duties should ensure that:

(a) lifeguards are not required to perform any other tasks which detract from the prime duty of supervising the pool;

(b) sufficient regular breaks are formalised in the work rota, to avoid the taking of informal and unannounced breaks during lifeguarding periods;

(c) where two or more lifeguards share poolside duties, consideration should be given to alternating duties (eg between a high chair, or patrolling) within the duty spell. Individuals' duty periods should preferably be overlapped, to maintain continuity of observation;

(d) where it is reasonably practicable* to meet the implied need for extra lifeguard training, vigilance may be assisted by rotating staff between lifeguarding and other duties (eg cashier, locker attendance) during the day.

Lifeguard numbers

203 Given the wide range of pool facilities, and of ways in which pools are used, it is not feasible to make specific recommendations for lifeguard numbers. Pool management should consider what is required, taking account of all relevant local circumstances at any particular time. The general arrangements decided upon should be set down in the written procedure.

204 As a starting point for managers' consideration, the following table sets out suggested minimum numbers of lifeguards for certain standard sizes of rectangular main pool, when used for general, public swimming, and without diving or other special equipment:

*See Introduction to the Guidance, paragraphs 5-6

38

Lifeguard numbers: basic guideline

Standard pool size: m	Area m²	Minimum number of lifeguards	Recommended minimum number of lifeguards in busy conditions
20.0 x 8.5	170	1	2
25.0 x 8.5	212	1	2
25.0 x 10.0	250	1	2
25.0 x 12.5	312	2	2
33.3 x 12.5	416	2	3

Notes

1   Where a single lifeguard is relied on, there should be adequate means of summoning assistance rapidly to the pool area (as recovering a casualty from the water often requires two people).

2   The figures in the fourth column are the recommended minimum whenever loading approaches pool maximum capacity (paragraphs 169-172).

3   For irregularly shaped pools including many leisure pools, the figures in the table, related to the water area shown in the second column, may be a useful starting point.

205   *Paragraphs 206-213 draw attention to various conditions of pool structure or use which may require more or fewer lifeguards, compared with the basic guideline.*

206   *Physically separate or 'hidden' areas of water.* Additional lifeguards may be required to cover all areas of water, including any which are physically separate, or 'hidden' by features.

207   *Depth of water.* Fewer lifeguards may be required where a pool contains only water of 1 m or less in depth. Conversely, the presence of water deeper than 2 m, or unusually extensive areas of deep water, may require additional supervision.

208   *'Programmed' sessions* (see paragraph 160(c)). The more disciplined nature of such activities, with the presence of group supervisors or club organisers, may make it possible to reduce the number of lifeguards, particularly where the group has exclusive use of the pool.

209   *School swimming lessons.* A particular example of 'programmed' swimming is where a public pool is used for swimming lessons conducted by a teacher employed by a school or Local Education Authority. Pool management will need to agree in advance with the organiser who will provide the necessary lifeguarding cover, and the numbers of lifeguards required. (See also general advice on arrangements for hire to outside organisations, in paragraphs 176-178 and Appendix 6.)

210   The lifeguarding function can in principle be provided by the teacher or instructor with a class, provided they have the full range of lifeguarding skills (as relevant to the particular pool) listed in paragraphs 190-191. (Relevant training is provided by the organisations listed in Appendix 7.) Where a class is divided into groups supervised by different teachers, whether it is sufficient for only one teacher to have full lifeguarding skills needs to be considered, according to all the circumstances. In particular, the area and depth of water to be covered, the ages and swimming abilities of pupils, and the numbers being supervised, are relevant. All those supervising should know and understand the pool's emergency procedures.

211   Advice on all aspects of the conduct of school groups is contained in the Department of Education and Science Safety Series No 4 *Safety in physical education*, obtainable from HMSO[107]; and in *Safe practice in physical education*, published by the British Association of Advisers and Lecturers in Physical Education[108].

212   *Food and alcohol etc.* Where food and alcohol are provided at the poolside, extra supervision is likely to be needed; see further paragraphs 218-219 below.

213   *Equipment, or specialised activities.* Where certain types of equipment are in use (or specialised activities in progress), extra supervision may be required: either dedicated, or to allow for the higher general vigilance required. More detailed advice on supervision of certain types of equipment is given in the following chapter (which also deals with the design

of equipment). Supervision of specialised activities is discussed below.

SUPERVISION REQUIREMENTS FOR SPECIALISED ACTIVITIES

Canoeing, and sub-aqua

214 Lifeguards require specialised skills to supervise these activities adequately. Organisations which can advise are listed in Appendix 7.

215 Consideration should be given to protecting the pool finishes from damage. Canoes should have rubber protection on bow and stern to prevent damage (or injury). Also, the edge of the pool should be protected to prevent damage while canoes are 'seal-launched'.

216 Protectors are available for sub-aqua cylinders and weight belts which, if dropped, could damage the pool bottom.

217 Where a pool has been used for such an activity and there is a possibility of damage, eg broken tiles, its condition should be checked before bathers are readmitted.

Sale of food and drink; associated social events

218 There should be specific supervision of areas where alcohol may be consumed, given both the possible effects on swimming ability, and the greater risks of unruliness. During social events (eg 'disco- swimming'), where high excitement will be generated, particularly careful supervision is necessary. *It is strongly advised that activities in the water take place before food or drink are consumed, to avoid the increased risk of drowning.*

219 Drinks by the pool should be in unbreakable containers.

EQUIPMENT PROVIDED
FOR BATHERS' USE

EQUIPMENT PROVIDED FOR BATHERS' USE

INTRODUCTION

220 This chapter advises on the safe design of various types of equipment provided for bathers' use and on the special supervision arrangements which may be required. The chapter does not cover certain types of newer equipment - wild water channels, water mushrooms, moveable pool floors etc - of which only limited evaluation has yet been possible.

221 The design of pool surrounds, and the positioning of features such as wave machine chambers, water slides or plants, should allow for adequate poolside supervision. Lifeguards should be able to see all parts of the pool (including those parts to which bathers should not have access: for example, over wave machine chambers). They should be able to reach quickly, bring to the side and land any bather in difficulty.

222 Where visibility or access are restricted by features (eg because lengths of surround are blocked off by a water slide structure), additional lifeguards may be needed (see paragraph 206). Lifeguards should be briefed on the best positions for supervision, for gaining access to the water and for taking a casualty out of the pool (in many leisure pools, this will be the beach area).

DIVING EQUIPMENT

Design

223 Whenever possible in existing swimming pools and in all new pools, diving stages and springboards should be installed over separate purpose-designed pools. This avoids the risks of collision between bathers and divers, and of weak or non-swimmers straying into very deep water.

224 It is essential that diving facilities are designed to provide adequate clearances from surrounding structures, and that the depth of water is sufficient in relation to the height and spring of the board. Facilities for competitive diving are required, for these purposes, to comply with the dimensional standards set by the Amateur Swimming Association (ASA) (for domestic competitions), or with those of the world governing body, the Federation Internationale de Natation Amateur (FINA) (for international competitions). There are slight differences between these standards: details are in Appendix 8. Either set of standards provides adequate safety for recreational diving in purpose-designed pools.

225 In addition, the ASA have recommended the standards set out in Appendix 8 for the shorter boards commonly used for recreational diving. Restricting the board length lessens the likelihood of increased diving velocity resulting from a running take-off.

226 If the height of a fixed diving stage falls between two of the specified heights in the relevant table in Appendix 8, then the higher standard, in terms of clearances etc, should be provided. Similarly, with springboards of less than 1 m in height above the water surface, the standards for a 1 m board should be met. Equipment which does not meet the relevant standards should be taken out of use, or brought up to standard.

227 Wherever possible diving equipment should be located in positions which avoid distractions to the diver. Sources of distraction may include glare and reflection from natural or artificial light, the movement of spectators etc, and activities in the pool. Divers should however be able to see clearly - and be seen by - bathers in the water. Wherever reasonably practicable*, steps for leaving the pool should be accessible by divers without their having to swim beneath the boards.

228 Diving boards, stages or platforms should be of sound construction, adequate strength, and protected against corrosion. They should be well maintained. Surfaces should be slip-resistant. Suitable access should be provided by steps or ladders.

229 Platforms more than 2 m above the poolside should have suitable guard and mid-rails to prevent users from falling from open edges to the pool side. Barriers should not obstruct the lifeguard's view of the platform. The only

*See Introduction to the Guidance, paragraphs 5-6

opening in the rails, other than the means of access, should be above the pool water.

230 Poolside starting platforms provided for competition use can be removable or integrated with the pool structure. Integral platforms may be preferred by some pool operators, because removable platforms require fitting and removal, occupy storage space, and may damage tiled surfaces. However, the platforms may provide an elevation of 500 mm to 700 mm above the water level which, if used by an unskilled person for diving into shallow water, risks too steep an entry. It is therefore recommended that permanent platforms should not be provided in new pools, except those intended for competition/training. If provided for these types of use, the platforms should be fitted with removable covers which can be used to prevent their use for diving during general bathing sessions.

231 Raised pool ends, to which starting platforms can be fixed, have been used in a number of deck level pools. These provide a permanent turning panel for both training and competitive swimming events. Precautions should be taken to prevent casual bathers from jumping or diving from their top edges, which could be dangerous.

232 Portable platforms should only be installed for:

(a) practising racing dives under skilled supervision; or

(b) use in swimming competitions of a standard where competitors are likely to be skilled in their use.

233 Where the removal of fixed platforms or raised pool ends is not reasonably practicable*, this area of the pool should be carefully supervised.

Supervision

234 Diving equipment should be directly supervised. The objectives are to ensure that it is used correctly and safely, and that swimmers and divers do not endanger each other. Where equipment is positioned over an unsegregated area of a main pool, additional supervision is likely to be required.

235 Pool operators should consider whether diving from the poolside needs to be restricted to avoid the risks either of diving into insufficient depth of water, or of collisions. Raised pool ends, or starting platforms permanently in position, pose special risks requiring extra vigilance (see paragraphs 230-231 above).

236 Suitable warning notices should be posted (see paragraphs 37-38). On occasion, it may be necessary to suspend diving over main pools, if increased pool use adds to the risk of collisions.

237 Rescues from deep diving pools (more than 4 m) may require special equipment. The rescue procedure should be set out in the emergency plan.

WATER SLIDES

238 The following advice applies to slides which begin more than 2 m above the surface of the landing pool (or main pool, if a separate landing pool is not provided) and may be capable of generating high descent speeds. (In general, it does not apply to the small, simple type of slide - used mainly by children - accessed by a ladder with no 'launch area' as such, and discharging direct into the main pool.) A slide may be provided singly, or as part of a multiple unit; and may be straight or incorporate bends. A flowing water film is usually provided to reduce friction. Some of the advice may be relevant to other slides (eg where mats are the sole means of sliding, or where high descent speeds are not generated), if there is a risk of accidents of any of the types listed in the next paragraph.

239 Water slides have been a frequent source of minor injuries, and some drownings have occurred following use. A combination of correct design and maintenance of the equipment, and supervision of its use, is essential to avoid the following types of accident:

(a) slips and falls on stairways leading to the top of the slide and on entering the top of the slide or leaving the landing pools;

(b) falls out of an open slide;

*See Introduction to the Guidance, paragraphs 5-6

(c) collisions between bathers either on the slide or in the landing pool;

(d) collisions between bathers and parts of the structure, including the slide wall, the base of the slide itself, and the landing pool walls; or

(e) abrasions and cuts from arm or torso contact with the wall edge of the flume or the leading edge of tunnels during descent.

240 Minor injuries are a possible warning that - given the height of many structures and the speeds attained - more serious ones could easily occur. Causes of incidents should be investigated and, if appropriate, use of the slide suspended while improvements are made.

Design

241 The water slide installation should ideally be designed as an integral part of the overall building design. The supporting structure should be designed in accordance with good engineering practice, be of sound construction, and capable of withstanding all foreseeable loads, including queueing loads. Structures installed indoors should be capable of withstanding the potentially corrosive atmosphere. Outdoors structures should be adequately protected against external environmental conditions.

242 There should be adequate maintenance procedures, set down in writing (preferably prepared by a structural engineer for the slide supporting structure, and by the slide manufacturer/designer for the slide itself). The procedures should specify the appropriate inspection intervals. The condition of the slide itself should be checked daily, before opening.

243 All parts of the structure should be adequately lit, for access and for maintenance purposes.

244 The following points should be considered in designing safe access:

(a) the staircase should be wide enough to allow convenient access to slides (whether single or multiple), and to avoid over-long queues. At a minimum, there should be room for two people to pass each other (for example, to allow access or egress of staff). An over-wide stair should be avoided, as erratic movements by children during busy periods could be hazardous;

Slide installation discharging into a self-contained landing pool

(b) half landings should be provided to break up straight lengths of stairs;

(c) circular staircases may be more hazardous during busy periods;

(d) staircase treads, half landings and launch areas should have slip-resistant surfaces;

(e) for open stairs, the balustrading should be strong enough to withstand forces likely to be applied;

(f) the layout of the launch area should allow safe access to the slide and should be large enough for staff to control riders' access to the slide;

(g) information notices on how the slide should be used should be prominently displayed;

(h) the slide entrance should be safe, and slide users should be prevented from running onto the slide, by a padded overhead bar or other means.

245 Interior surfaces should be as smooth as possible. Any slight variation at the joint positions will jolt the rider.

There should be no sharp edges or abrasive surfaces which might injure riders. The slide should be watertight, and all surfaces should be inert, non-toxic and capable of being easily cleaned.

246 Open slides should be designed to prevent riders from being ejected at any point when the slide is properly used. The angle of descent, the trough profile, the bend contours, the water flow rate and the height of the slide walls should all be designed to ensure that riders are adequately contained within the slideway throughout the length of travel.

247 It is impossible, with an open slide, absolutely to prevent a rider from standing up and possibly falling out. Fully enclosed slides, or tubes, will prevent this, but have the disadvantage of restricting supervision during the ride. Some limited supervision is possible where tubes are made of translucent material, though any twists and turns in the slide will restrict visibility. Whether open or closed, slides should be designed

Leisure pool with a wave machine in operation

so that riders are not thrown with excessive force against the sliding surface. Undulations which cause bathers to strike the top of an enclosed tube, or lose contact and control on an open slide, should be avoided.

248 Suitable handholds should be provided at the starting position so that bathers may position themselves for descent. The entry point design should prevent running starts, and should be supervised. A traffic lights system may be useful for spacing slide riders, but should only be used in addition to, and not in place of, supervision. Suitable communication equipment will be required unless the layout is such that good visual and verbal communication can be maintained between supervisors at the top and bottom of the slide.

249 Except where a run-out area is provided (see paragraph 253), the slide should discharge into either a separate landing pool or a physically separated area of the swimming pool (to avoid collisions with other bathers). The gradient of the lower section of the slideway should not be too steep; it is important that bathers do not enter the water too quickly. The end of the slide should deliver the rider to approximately the water level within the landing pool. However, for installations in existing pools, the slide may terminate above pool water level. In these cases, the depth of water will need to be considered in relation to the height of the slide above water level and advice should be sought from the slide manufacturer/designer.

250 Landing pools should be carefully designed, to ensure that bathers enter safely and can leave quickly to avoid the risk of collision with following riders. There should be sufficient horizontal clearance between the pool sides and the end of the slide, and a water depth of at least 1 m. See Appendix 9 for suggested dimensions for landing pools. (These take the German DIN standard as their starting point. There is as yet no British Standard for the design of water slides or landing pools.) The bottom of the landing pool should be smooth, without any projections or sharp edges. Gratings should not be provided in the floor area

of the pool where riders are projected from the slide. Exit steps should have slip-resistant surfaces, and be fitted with handrails.

251 Adequate water quality and clarity, at least equal to standards for a conventional swimming pool (see paragraphs 108-157), should be maintained in the landing pool. A high rate of water turnover, good filtration, and a high rate of disinfection will often be necessary, especially with an outdoor slide.

252 The use of special effects (eg coloured flashing lights) requires careful consideration. This could be hazardous if, for example, it increases the likelihood that riders will become disorientated.

253 A recent development in slide design has been the introduction of a run-out area at the end of the slide to replace the landing pool. The device, called an 'Aquacatch', contains very shallow flowing water and its base is at the same level as the end section of the slide. It is understood that this method is particularly designed to be safer for younger/smaller children.

Supervision

254 The excitement of using a slide may encourage bathers, particularly youngsters, to experiment or 'show off' in ways which add to the excitement, but can be extremely dangerous to themselves and others. Close supervision is required, particularly to discourage the following kinds of behaviour which have contributed to accidents:

(a) going down in pairs, or chains, or one rider too close to the next;

(b) riders stopping themselves or slowing themselves down (for example this is possible where an open slide enters a covered section);

(c) standing up on the slide;

(d) failing to leave the landing pool immediately on arrival.

255 Supervision arrangements for the slide should take account of any advice from the manufacturer. Suitable instructions and warning notices should be displayed. Both entry and landing

points should be supervised (with good communication between them: see paragraph 248) whenever the slide is in use; at other times, access should be prevented.

256 The supervisor should control entry so that riders are adequately spaced. This is both to avoid collisions on the slide, and to allow sufficient time for a rider to move away from the discharge point in the landing area. The appropriate time interval for each slide will depend both on the weight of the riders, and the method of travel adopted, eg sitting upright or lying flat.

257 The supervisor controlling the entry point should stop users making a running start, thereby gaining excessive speed. The method of travel recommended by the manufacturer should be followed. At busy periods, the supervisor should ensure there is an orderly queue, to prevent pushing which could lead to falls.

258 The lifeguard at the discharge point

should ensure that riders move quickly out of the path of the slide. Careful vigilance is needed because riders, particularly children, may be disorientated; moreover, turbulence may make bathers difficult to see. Injuries should be attended to immediately, but without detracting from supervision.

WAVE MACHINES

Design

259 Wave machines are found in many leisure pools. The design of the wave formation and of the pool should be considered together, to minimise the risk of bathers being thrown against fixed parts of the structure (eg pool access points, steps or stairways), whilst the machinery is operating.

260 The height of the wave generated will vary with the type of equipment installed and its particular application. As a consequence, the height of the pool

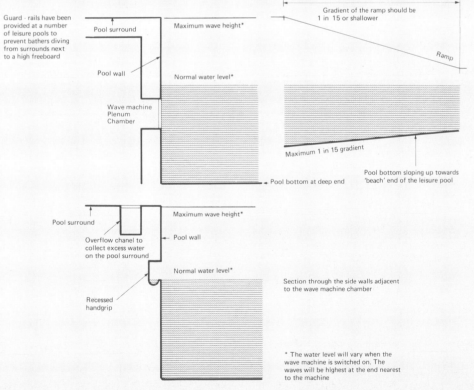

Fig 4 Cross sections through the end and side walls of a typical leisure pool tank with a wave machine.
Note particularly that:
(i)   ramps which could be a hazard when wet should not have a gradient steeper than 1 in 15. A 1 in 20 gradient is preferred (see paragraph 31):
(ii) there is a hand grip recessed into the pool wall (see paragraph 260);
(iii) depending on the size of wave generated, the pool surround/freeboard may need to be higher than in conventional pools (see paragraph 260).

surround above the water (or freeboard) will also vary, but in certain areas, it will be higher than would be found around a conventional rectangular pool. The increased height of surrounds may make it difficult for some bathers to leave the pool quickly using the pool edge; it is recommended that a recessed handgrip or ledge be provided around the pool perimeter adjacent to the wave machine chamber. There are also implications for supervision (see paragraph 264).

261   Any parts of the machinery located in the water should be designed wherever possible so that there are no trapping points between fixed and moving parts. Where trapping points cannot be eliminated by design, they should be suitably guarded.

262   Unauthorised access to wave-generating machinery should be prevented. All motors, shafts, gears, pulleys, chains, sprockets and similar moving parts should be totally enclosed by guards, which must be kept in position whenever the machinery is in motion. There is a British Standard on safeguarding machinery[31].

Supervision

263   A safe procedure should be devised for operating the wave mechanism. This should preferably cover:

(a)   prior audible and visible warnings, to enable bathers to move clear of the area in front of it;

(b)   intervals between successive operations, to enable lifeguards to scrutinise the bottom of the pool. (Where, exceptionally, the wave machine operates continuously, additional supervision may be needed);

(c)   ensuring that the machine can be switched off quickly in an emergency.

264   Supervision should be from the sides, in order to see between the waves. Particularly careful vigilance will be required in view of the extra risks arising from:

(a)   large influxes of bathers into the water, when the machine is to be operated;

(b)   high excitement, and possible disorientation, especially among young children;

(c)   bathers jumping from pool surrounds or freeboards (given that these may be higher than in a conventional pool - see paragraph 260 - and that water depth may be difficult to judge while the wave machine is operating). Diving while the wave machine is operating is dangerous and should not be allowed.

Bathers should be alerted that the waves will make swimming harder. Non-swimmers and weak swimmers should stay well within their depth.

INFLATABLE PLAY STRUCTURES AND OTHER FLOATING PLATFORMS

Design

265   Various types of floating play structures are available. The Institute of Baths and Recreation Management have issued advice on their use[109]. Care should be taken not to use types which could trap bathers underneath. Larger inflatables should be tethered to prevent them moving in the pool. The means of anchorage/tethering should not be a hazard to bathers.

266   All floating equipment should be carefully positioned so that bathers cannot fall from the equipment to the pool side or strike the pool edge. Certain large inflatable devices are unsuitable for small swimming pools where adequate clearance between the floating platform and the pool edge cannot be maintained. The equipment should be in sufficiently deep water, so that a bather who falls off will not be injured by striking the pool bottom.

267   Underwater lights may be helpful in ensuring that any bather underneath the equipment can be seen. Inflatables are likely to require direct supervision, given that they restrict vision through the water, and that they encourage bathers to congregate in a small area. Attention should be paid to the possible risks from entanglement; or from diving from a raised structure into insufficient depth of water.

APPENDICES

APPENDIX 1

MEMBERSHIP OF INDEPENDENT WORKING PARTY CHAIRED BY HSE

Mr P Bright
National Union of Public Employees

Mr T H Cooper
Amateur Swimming Association

Mr H T Hitchin
Institute of Baths and Recreation Management and Institute of Leisure and Amenity Management

Mr D R Pimblett
General Municipal Boilermakers & Allied Trades Union

Mr H Rigby
Association of Metropolitan Authorities

Mr K H Sach
Royal Life Saving Society UK

Mr N Winter
Association of District Councils

Representatives from HSE included:

Mr T D Beals
Mr B W McCordall
HM Factory Inspectorate: National Industry Group for Entertainment and Local Government

Miss E Gyngell
Local Authority Unit

Note: The Working Party was appointed by a meeting of some 25 industry and safety organisations, convened by HSE in July 1985.

APPENDIX 2

SAFETY SIGNS

The requirements of the Safety Signs Regulations 1980

These regulations set out a system for signs which give a health and safety message by the use of a combination of geometrical shape, colour and pictorial symbol.

The signs must conform to Part I of BS 5378, published on 31 July 1980.

A guide to the requirements of the Regulations is obtainable from HMSO[110].

Examples of signs based upon the Safety Signs Regulations

These examples from RoSPA's National Water Safety Committee show how the principles of the Safety Signs Regulations may be applied to safety in the swimming pool. The same principles may be applied to other swimming pool activities not covered here. The signs shown have a red border with a symbol in black on a white background.

APPENDIX 3

REPORTING ACCIDENTS · LEGAL REQUIREMENTS

Employers and others in charge of pools have duties under the Reporting of Injuries, Diseases and Dangerous Occurrences Regulations 1985 to report accidents to the enforcing authority (the Health and Safety Executive or the local authority - see paragraph 11 of the Introduction).

In particular:

> if anyone working at the pool or any member of the public on the premises dies or is seriously injured as a result of activities at the pool, the employer or person in charge of the pool must immediately notify the enforcing

authority by the quickest practicable means (normally by 'phone). This must be followed up within seven days by a written report of the incident. Form F2508, obtainable from HMSO, must be used.

The employer must also send a report on form F2508 to the enforcing authority within seven days if he or any of his employees are off work for more than three consecutive days (including normal days off) as a result of an accident at the pool.

A record of any reported incident must be kept on the premises.

Further information on duties under the Regulations can be obtained from HSE Area Offices. HSE have published a free leaflet, and a more detailed guide[111,112].

APPENDIX 4

SWIMMING POOL USERS' SAFETY CODE

1 Spot the dangers

Take care, swimming pools can be hazardous. Water presents a risk of drowning, and injuries can occur from hitting the hard surrounds, or from misuse of equipment.

2 Always swim within your ability

Never swim after a heavy meal or after alcohol. Avoid holding your breath and swimming long distances under water. Be especially careful if you have a medical condition such as epilepsy, asthma, diabetes or a heart condition.

3 Check new places

Every pool is different, so always make sure you know how deep the water is, and check for other hazards such as diving boards, water slides and steep slopes into deeper water etc.

4 Take safety advice

Follow advice provided for your and others' safety. Avoid unruly behaviour which can be dangerous: for instance, running on the side of the pool; ducking; acrobatics in the water; or shouting or screaming (which could distract attention from an emergency). Always do as the lifeguards say, and remember that a moment of foolish behaviour can cost a life.

5 Look out for yourself and other swimmers

It is safer to swim with a companion. Keep an eye open for others, particularly young children and non-swimmers.

6 Learn how to help

If you see somebody in difficulty, get help immediately. In an emergency, keep calm and do exactly as you are told.

Acknowledgements

We gratefully acknowledge the help of the Royal Society for the Prevention of Accidents in preparing this Safety Code.

APPENDIX 5

POOL WRITTEN OPERATING PROCEDURES: Check-list

Normal operating plan

(a)   Details of the pool, including for example pool dimensions, and a plan of the building;

(b)   potential risk factors;

(c)   dealing with the public (safety education; controlling access; etc);

(d)   maximum bather loads;

(e)   first aid supplies and training;

(f)   conditions for hire to outside organisations;

(g)   details of alarm systems and any emergency equipment; maintenance arrangements;

(h)   the lifeguard's duties as well as any special supervision requirements for equipment etc;

(i)   systems of work, including:

   (i)   lines of supervision;

   (ii)   call out procedures;

   (iii) work rotation (if applicable);

   (iv)   maximum poolside work times;

(j)   lifeguard training;

(k)   numbers of lifeguards for particular activities.

Emergency action plan

Action to be taken in the event of a foreseeable emergency, for example:

(a)   overcrowding;

(b)   disorderly behaviour;

(c)   lack of water clarity;

(d)   outbreak of fire (or sounding of alarm to evacuate the building);

(e)   bomb threat;

(f)   lighting failure;

(g)   structural failure;

(h)   emission of toxic gases;

(i)   serious injury to a bather;

(j)   discovery of a casualty in the water.

The procedure should make clear how, if it is necessary to clear the water or to evacuate the building, this is to be done.

Note   Detailed advice on many of these matters is in the Chapter 'Supervision arrangements to safeguard pool users' paragraphs 158-219.

APPENDIX 6

HIRE OF POOL TO OUTSIDE ORGANISATIONS: CHECK-LIST OF POINTS FOR INCLUSION IN CONTRACTS

1   Information on numbers participating and their swimming skills.

2   Name of hirer's representative who will be in charge of the group.

3   Numbers and skills/qualifications of lifeguards to be present during the session; and whether these will be provided by the hirer or by the pool operator.

4   Hirer to be given copies of normal and emergency operating procedures, and to sign to the effect that these have been read and understood.

5   Specific agreement on the respective responsibilities of the pool operator and the hirer for action in any emergency. A distinction needs to be drawn between:

(a)   emergencies arising from the activities of the group using the pool; and

(b)   other emergencies (structural or power failures, etc).

Responsibility for the latter will remain with the pool operator who will need, accordingly, to have competent staff in attendance during the hire session.

6   Any rules of behaviour to be enforced during the session.

7   Any advice on safety to be given to participants, eg on avoiding alcohol and food immediately before swimming.

APPENDIX 7

ORGANISATIONS WHO CAN ADVISE ON TRAINING OR GENERAL SAFETY MATTERS

Organisations providing first aid training:

St John Ambulance Association
1 Grosvenor Crescent
LONDON   SW1X 7EF

St Andrew Ambulance Association
St Andrew's House
Milton Street
GLASGOW   G4 OMR

British Red Cross Society
9 Grosvenor Crescent
LONDON   SW1X 7EJ

Organisation providing pool attendants and plant operators training:

Institute of Baths and Recreation Management
Giffard House
36/38 Sherrard Street
MELTON MOWBRAY
Leicester   LE13 1XJ

Organisations providing lifeguard or lifesaving training:

The Royal Life Saving Society UK
Mountbatten House
STUDLEY
Warwickshire   B80 7NN

In consultations on this document, the RLSS Pool Bronze Award was most frequently suggested as a suitable qualification for those providing a comprehensive lifeguarding service at a pool.

The RLSS and the Amateur Swimming Association recommend the joint ASA/RLSS Lifesaving Certificate for those in charge of groups during programmed swimming sessions.

Amateur Swimming Association
Harold Fern House
Derby Square
LOUGHBOROUGH
Leicester   LE11 OAL

Scottish Amateur Swimming Association
Airthey Castle
University of Stirling
STIRLING   FK9 LAE

The Swimming Teachers' Association
Birch Street
WALSALL
West Midlands   WS2 8HZ

Organisations who can advise on supervision of specialised activities:

British Canoe Union
Flexel House
45-47 High Street
Addlestone
WEYBRIDGE   KT15 1JV

British Sub-Aqua Club
16 Upper Woburn Place
LONDON   WCIH OQW

Scottish Canoe Association
18 Ainslie Place
EDINBURGH   EH3 6AU

Scottish Sub-Aqua Club
c/o Mr A Tison
16 Royal Cresent
GLASGOW   G32 9AA

Safety organisations

Royal Society for the Prevention of Accidents (RoSPA)
Head Office
Cannon House
The Priory
Queensway
BIRMINGHAM   B4 6BS

Scottish Accident Prevention Council
Water Leisure Safety Committee
Slateford House
53 Lanark Road
EDINBURGH   EH14 1TL

British Safety Council
National Safety Centre
62 Chancellors Road
LONDON   W6 9RS

APPENDIX 8

DIMENSIONS FOR DIVING EQUIPMENT

Recommended water depths and clearances for diving pools are given in Tables I and II and should be read in conjunction with paragraphs 223 to 237. These are based on the recommendations of the Amateur Swimming Association and are reproduced for the Sports Council's *Handbook of Sports and Recreational Building Design*[2]. Major international and competition facilities will have to meet the requirements of the international body, FINA (Federation Internationale de Natation Amateur), as shown in Table III. These are varied from time to time and the current recommendations should be checked with the Amateur Swimming Association.

TABLE I   COMPETITIVE DIVING

		Springboards		Fixed boards		
		m	m	m	m	m
A	Board height from water	1	3	5	7.5	10
B	Board length	4.8	4.8	5.0	6.0	6.0
C	Board width	0.5	0.5	2.0	2.0	2.0
D	Depth of water at plummet	3.0	3.5	3.8	4.1	4.5
E	Distance depth D maintained forward	5.3	6.0	6.0	8.0	10.5
F	Distance depth D maintained to sides	2.2	2.7	3.0	3.0	3.0
G	Clearance forward	7.5	9.0	10.5	11.0	13.5
H	Clearance to sides	2.5	3.5	3.8	4.5	4.5
I	Distance to adjacent board	2.5	2.5	2.5	2.5	2.5
J	Clearance behind	1.5	1.5	1.25	1.5	1.5
L	Clearance overhead	4.6	4.6	3.0	3.2	3.4
M	Clearance overhead maintained to sides	2.75	2.75	2.75	2.75	2.75
N	Clearance overhead maintained forward	5.0	5.0	5.0	5.0	6.0

Notes:

1   The table, shown above, incorporates the latest dimensions recommended by the ASA and includes, also, a column of dimensions for a 7.5 m platform height - this height is considered useful for highboard training. Designers should check with the ASA to establish whether the dimensions indicated in Tables I and II are their latest requirements.

2   A ± 0.1m tolerance is permissible on the nominal board height. All dimensions should relate to a central point at the front end of the diving board(s).

3   The platform thickness should not be greater than 0.2m at its front.

4   Designers should consider the current standards specified by FINA (Federation Internationale de Natation Amateur) if the pool is to be used for national/international standard events.

It is recommended that a diving pool should be separate from the main pool for obvious reasons, but where this is not possible, the board height of a springboard should be confined to 1m, and when in use, the area concerned should be roped off to avoid swimmers causing a safety hazard.

TABLE II   ASA RECREATIONAL DIVING (FIRM BOARDS)

		m	m	m	m	m	m	m
A	Board height from water	1	1	2	2	3	3	5
B	Board length	0.75	1.75	0.75	1.75	0.75	1.75	5.0
C	Board width	0.75	0.75	0.75	0.75	0.75	0.75	2.0
D	Depth of water at plummet	2.6	2.6	3.0	3.0	3.25	3.25	3.8
E	Distance depth D maintained forward	3.0	4.0	3.0	4.0	3.5	4.5	6.0
F	Distance depth D maintained to sides	2.2	2.2	2.4	2.4	2.6	2.6	3.0
G	Clearance forward	4.5	5.5	5.5	6.5	6.5	7.5	10.25
H	Clearance to sides	2.5	2.6	3.0	3.0	3.5	3.5	3.8
I	Distance to adjacent board	2.5	2.5	2.5	2.5	2.5	2.5	2.5
J	Clearance behind	1.25	1.25	1.25	1.25	1.25	1.25	1.25
K	Clearance behind board to wall	0.8	0.8	0.8	0.8	0.8	0.8	0.8
L	Clearance overhead	3.0	3.0	3.0	3.0	3.0	3.0	3.0

TABLE III   FINA DIVING REQUIREMENTS*

				Board height		
		1m	3m	5m	7.5m	10m
A	From plummet back to pool wall	0.75	1.25	1.25	1.5	1.5
AA	From plummet back to platform plummet			0.75/ 1.5	0.75/ 1.5	0.75/ 1.5
B	From plummet to pool wall at side	2.3	2.9	4.25	4.5	5.25
C	From plummet to adjacent plummet			5/3 = 2.1m 5/1 = 2.1m	7.5/5 = 2.5m 7.5/3/1 = 2.1m	10/7.5/5 = 2.75m 10/3or1 = 2.75m
D	From plummet to pool wall ahead	8.0	9.5	10.25	11.0	13.5
E	On plummet to ceiling overhead	3.0	3.0	3.0min (3.4pref)	3.2min (3.4pref)	3.4min (5.0pref)
F	Clear overhead, behind and each side of plummet	2.75	2.75	2.75	2.75	2.75
G	Clear overhead ahead of plummet	5.0	5.0	5.0	5.0	5.0
H	Depth of water at plummet	3.4	3.4	3.8min (4.0pref)	4.1min (4.5pref)	4.5min (5.0pref)
J/K	Distance and depth ahead of plummet	5.0dist 3.3depth	6.0 3.3	6.0 3.7/ (3.9pref)	8.0 4.0/ (4.4pref)	12.0 4.25/ (4.75pref)
L/M	Distance and depths each side of plummet	2.05dist 3.3depth	2.65 3.0	4.25 3.7/ (3.9pref)	4.5 4.0/ (4.4pref)	5.25 4.25/ (4.9pref)
N	Maximum angle of slope to reduce pool depth beyond full depth requirements			30 degrees		
P	Maximum angle of slope to reduce ceiling height beyond clear height requirements			30 degrees		

* For latest requirements, you are advised to check with ASA or FINA.

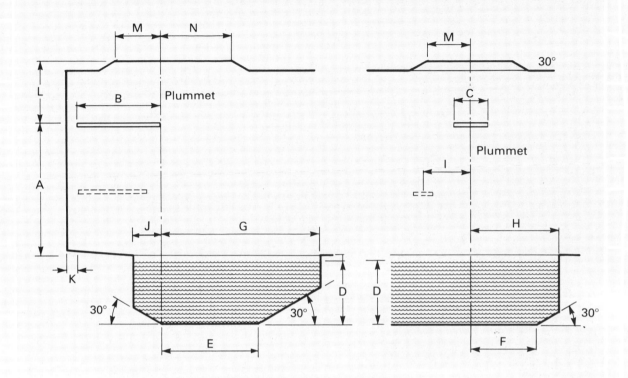

Fig 5 Sections of diving pools to be read in association with Tables I and II

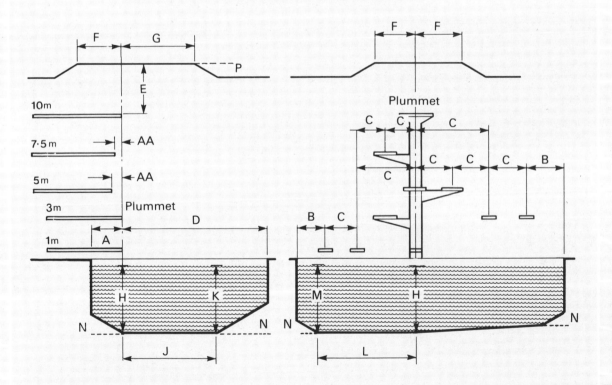

Fig 6 Sections of diving pools to be read in association with Table III showing FINA requirments

APPENDIX 9

LAYOUTS OF WATER SLIDE LANDING POOLS AND OTHER WATER AREAS USED FOR SINGLE AND TWIN SLIDE INSTALLATIONS

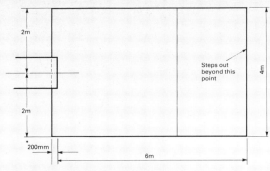

Fig 7 Single slide installation

NOTES

*There should be a 200 mm slide overhang.

Dimensions indicated are taken from German DIN 7937 (August 1987).

See section at Fig 10 for recommended profile showing water depth.

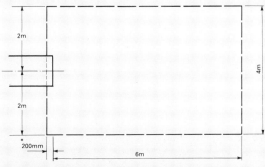

Fig 8 Single slide installation where slide terminates in a water area other than a landing pool

*200 mm minimum overhang.

A 6m x 4m water area is required clear of any obstructions or equipment.

A minimum water depth of 1m is required but this should be determined with the slide manufacturer/ supplier.

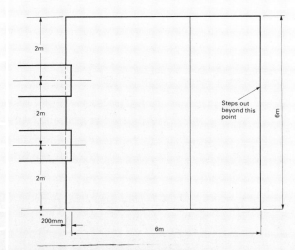

Fig 9 Twin slide installations

*200 mm minimum overhang.

This layout is not shown in German DIN 7937 (August 1987), but it has been approved by the German DIN office.

See section at Fig 10 for recommended profile showing water depth.

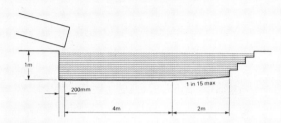

Fig 10

NOTES

The water depth shown is applicable to all slides which terminate 150 mm above or below water level.

German DIN 7937 (August 1987) recommends a minimum water depth of 1m and there is no mention of a sloping bottom.

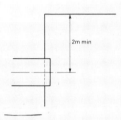

Fig 11

Where the slide terminates in a corner of a main pool or other water area, there should be 2m clear between the centre-line of the slide and adjacent pool edge. See Fig 8 for other dimensions.

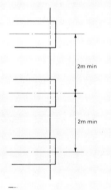

Fig 12

For multiple slide installations, the recommended dimension between the centre-line of each slide is 2m minimum. See Fig 9 for other dimensions.

The dimensions indicated apply to all conventional water slides (ie flume or tube) which do not terminate in a run out trough, 'aquacatch' or similar device.

NOTE: *All dimensions indicated are advisory only.* The slide design/configuration should determine the dimensions of the landing pool and distances between slides for multiple slide installations. The slide designer/manufacturer/supplier should be asked to stipulate the minimum safe dimensions for a given installation.

APPENDIX 10

LIST OF SPORTS COUNCILS AND HSE ADDRESSES AND ENQUIRY POINTS

Sports Council addresses

Sports Council Headquarters
16 Upper Woburn Place
London WC1H OQP
TEL: 01-388 1277

Northern Region
Aykley Heads
Durham DH1 5UU
Tel: 091-384 9595

North West Region
Astley House
Quay Street
Manchester M3 4AE
Tel: 061-834 0338

Yorkshire & Humberside Region
Coronet House
Queen Street
Leeds LS1 4PW
Tel: 0532 436443

Greater London and South East Region
PO Box 480
Crystal Palace NSC
London SE19 2BQ
Tel: 01-778 8600

Southern Region
51A Church Street
Caversham
Reading
Berkshire RG4 8AX
Tel: 0734 483311

East Midlands Region
Grove House
Bridgford Road
West Bridgford
Nottingham NG2 6AP
Tel: 0602 821887/822586

West Midlands Region
Metropolitan House
1 Hagley Road
Five Ways
Birmingham B16 8TT
Tel: 021-454 3808

Eastern Region
26/8 Bromham Road
Bedford MK40 2QP
Tel: 0234 45222

South Western Region
Ashlands House
Ashlands
Crewkerne
Somerset TA18 7LQ
Tel: 0460 73491

Sports Council for Wales
National Sports Centre for Wales
Sophia Gardens
Cardiff CF1 9SW
Tel: 0222 397571

Scottish Sports Council
1 St Colme Street
Edinburgh EH3 6AA
Tel: 031-225 8411

Sports Council for Northern Ireland
2a Upper Malone Road
Belfast BT9 5LA
Tel: 0232 381222

HSE Public Enquiry Points (PEPs)

There are three public enquiry points based in HSE's Library and Information Services at London, Sheffield and Bootle. They are open between 10 am and 3 pm, Monday to Friday. The fourth PEP is Prestel which is available 24 hours a day.

The regional locations for PEPs allow cheaper telephone access. Their addresses and telephone numbers are as follows:

Health and Safety Executive
Library and Information Services
Broad Lane
Sheffield S3 7HQ
Tel: 0742 752539
Telex: 54556

Health and Safety Executive
Library and Information Services
St Hugh's House
Stanley Precinct
Trinity Road
Bootle
Merseyside L20 3QY
Tel: 051-951 4381
Telex: 628235

Health and Safety Executive
Library and Information Services
Baynards House
1 Chepstow Place
Westbourne Grove
London W2 4TF
Tel: 01-221 0870
Telex: 25683

HSE addresses

Health and Safety Executive
Baynards House
1 Chepstow Place
Westbourne Grove
London W2 4TF
(Tel: 01-229 3456)

Area Offices

SOUTH WEST (Avon, Cornwall, Devon,
Gloucestershire, Somerset, Isles of Scilly)
Inter City House
Mitchell Lane
Victoria Street
Bristol BS1 6AN
(Tel: 0272 290681)

SOUTH (Berkshire, Dorset, Hampshire, Isle
of Wight, Wiltshire)
Priestley House
Priestley Road
Basingstoke RG24 9NW
(Tel: 0256 473181)

SOUTH EAST
(Kent, Surrey, East Sussex, West Sussex)
3 East Grinstead House
London Road
East Grinstead
West Sussex RH19 1RR
(Tel: 0342 26922)

LONDON NORTH
(Barking and Dagenham, Barnet, Brent,
Camden, Ealing, Enfield, Hackney,
Haringey, Harrow, Havering, Islington,
Newham, Redbridge, Tower Hamlets,
Waltham Forest)
Maritime House
1 Linton Road
Barking Essex IG11 8HF
(Tel: 01-594 5522)

LONDON SOUTH (Bexley, Bromley, City
of London, Croydon, Greenwich,
Hammersmith and Fulham, Hillingdon,
Hounslow, Kensington and Chelsea,
Kingston, Lambeth, Lewisham, Merton,
Richmond, Southwark, Sutton,
Wandsworth, Westminster)
1 Long Lane
London SE1 4PG
(Tel: 01-407 8911)

EAST ANGLIA (Essex, Norfolk, Suffolk)
39 Baddow Road
Chelmsford
Essex CM2 OHL
(Tel: 0245 24661)

NORTHERN HOME COUNTIES
(Bedfordshire, Buckinghamshire,
Cambridgeshire, Hertfordshire)
14 Cardiff Road
Luton
Beds LU1 1PP
(Tel: 0582 34121)

EAST MIDLANDS (Leicestershire,
Northamptonshire, Oxfordshire,
Warwickshire)
5th Floor Belgrave House
1 Greyfriars
Northampton NN1 2BS
(Tel: 0604 21233)

WEST MIDLANDS (West Midlands)
McLaren Building
2 Masshouse Circus
Queensway
Birmingham B4 7NP
(Tel: 021-200 2299)

WALES (Clwyd, Dyfed, Gwent, Gwynedd,
Mid Glamorgan, Powys, South Glamorgan,
West Glamorgan)
Brunel House
2 Fitzalan Road
Cardiff CF2 1SH
(Tel: 0222 473777)

THE MARCHES (Hereford and Worcester,
Shropshire, Staffordshire)
The Marches House
Midway
Newcastle-under-Lyme
Staffs ST5 1DT
(Tel: 0782 717181)

NORTH MIDLANDS (Derbyshire,
Lincolnshire, Nottinghamshire)
Birbeck House
Trinity Square
Nottingham NG1 4AU
(Tel: 0602 470712)

SOUTH YORKSHIRE (Humberside, South
Yorkshire)
Sovereign House
40 Silver Street
Sheffield S1 2ES
(Tel: 0742 739081)

W & N YORKS (North Yorkshire, West
Yorkshire)
8 St Paul's Street
Leeds LS1 2LE
(Tel: 0532 446191)

GREATER MANCHESTER (Greater Manchester)
Quay House
Quay Street
Manchester M3 3JB
(Tel: 061-831 7111)

MERSEYSIDE (Cheshire, Merseyside)
The Triad
Stanley Road
Bootle
Merseyside L20 3PG
(Tel: 051-922 7211)

NORTH WEST (Cumbria, Lancashire)
Victoria House
Ormskirk Road
Preston PR1 1HH
(Tel: 0772 59321)

NORTH EAST (Cleveland, Durham, Northumberland, Tyne & Wear)
Arden House
Regent Centre
Regent Farm Road
Gosforth
Newcastle-upon-Tyne NE3 3JN
(Tel: 091-284 8448)

SCOTLAND EAST (Borders, Central, Fife, Grampian, Highland, Lothian, Tayside and the island areas of Orkney and Shetland)
Belford House
59 Belford Road
Edinburgh EH4 3UE
(Tel: 031-225 1313)

SCOTLAND WEST (Dumfries and Galloway, Strathclyde, and the Western Isles)
Royal Exchange Assurance House
314 St Vincent Street
Glasgow G3 8XG
(Tel: 041-204 2646)

REFERENCES

REFERENCES

Note: References published by the British Standards Institution (BSI) can be ordered from BSI Sales Department, Linford Wood, Milton Keynes MK14 6LE. Alternatively personal callers can buy them at any of the following sales outlets: 195 Pentonville Road, London N1; Hampden House, 61 Green Street, London W1; or 3 York Street, Manchester.

1 *Water Safety Outdoors - Advisory notes for Local Authorities and others* Obtainable from the Royal Society for the Prevention of Accidents, Cannon House, The Priory, Queensway, Birmingham B4 6BS

2 *Handbook of Sports and Recreational Building Design* - Volume 1 - *Ice Rinks and Swimming Pools* ISBN O 85139 586 4; Architectural Press Limited, 9 Queen Anne's Gate, London SWIH 9BY

3 *Sports Council Standardised Approach to Sports Halls (SASH) Design Guide 2: swimming pool option* Available from the Sports Council, 16 Upper Woburn Place, London WC1H OQP

4 BS 5395: 1977 (Parts 1 and 2) *Code of Practice for the design of straight helical and spiral stairs* BSI

5 BS 6180: 1982 *Code of Practice for protective barriers in and about buildings* BSI

6 The Offices, Shops and Railway Premises (Hoists and Lifts) Regulations 1968, SI 1968 No 849 ISBN 0 11 080849 5 HMSO

7 HSE Guidance Note PM 34 *Safety in the use of escalators* ISBN 0 11 883572 6 HMSO

8 HSE Guidance Note PM 45 *Escalators: periodic thorough examination* ISBN 0 11 883595 5 HMSO

9 BS 6206: 1981 *Specification for impact performance requirements for flat safety glass and safety plastics for use in buildings* BSI

10 CIBSE Guide Obtainable from Chartered Institution of Building Services Engineers, Delta House, 222 Balham High Road, London SW12 9BS

11 British Standards Code of Practice BS8233: 1987 *Sound insulation and noise reduction* BSI

12 *The Safety Signs Regulations 1980* SI 1980 No 1471 ISBN 0 11 007471 8 HMSO

13 HSE Guidance Note PM 5 *Automatically controlled steam and hot water boilers* ISBN 0 11 883050 3 HMSO

14 British Gas *Automatic flue dampers for use with gas-fired space heating and water heating appliances* Obtainable from British Gas, 59 Bryanston Street, London W2 2AZ

15 HSE Cautionary Notice SHW 2125 *Danger of explosion in oil fuel storage tanks fitted with immersed heaters* ISBN 0 11 883088 0 HMSO

16 HSE Guidance Booklet HS(G) 34 *Storage of LPG at fixed installations* ISBN 0 11 883908 X HMSO

17 HSE Guidance Note CS 4 *The keeping of LPG in cylinders and similar containers* ISBN 0 11 883373 1 HMSO

18 HSE Guidance Note CS 2 *The storage of highly flammable liquids* ISBN 0 11 883027 9 HMSO

19 Sports Council/TUS Energy Data Sheet No 4 *Ventilation* Available free from the address at reference 3 above

20 Sports Council/TUS Energy Data Sheet No 5 *Dehumidification and air conditioning* Available free from the address at reference 3 above

21 ACGIH *Industrial ventilation - A manual of recommended practice* American Conference of Governmental Industrial Hygienists ISBN 0 93671 26 5 Available from ACGIH, 6500 Glenway Buildings D/7, Cincinnatti, Ohio, USA

22 BS 5720: 1979 *Code of Practice for mechanical ventilation and air conditioning of buildings* BSI

23 BS 5925: 1980 *Code of Practice for design of buildings: ventilation principles and designing for natural ventilation* BSI

24 CIBSE *Lighting Guide - Sports* (address as at reference 10)

25 CIBSE *Code for interior lighting* (address as at reference 10)

26 *Lighting for Swimming Pools* CIE Publication No 62 (1984) from International Commission on Illumination, Bureau Central de la CIE, 52 Boulevard Malesherbes, 75008, Paris, France

27 BS 5266: Parts 1 and 3 *Emergency Lighting* BSI

28 BS 6423: 1983 *Code of Practice for maintenance of electrical switchgear and controlgear for voltages up to and including 650 V* BSI

29 BS 6626: 1985 *Code of Practice for maintenance of electrical switchgear and controlgear for voltages above 650 V and up to and including 36 kV* BSI

30 *Regulations for electrical installations* ISBN 0 85 296235 5 Published by the Institution of Electrical Engineers, PO Box 26, Hitchin, Herts SG5 1SA

31 BS 5304: 1975 *Code of Practice for safeguarding of machinery* BSI

32 BS 4343: 1968 *Industrial plugs, sockets outlets and couplers for AC and DC supplies* BSI

33 International Electrotechnical Committee Publication 364 Available from IEC, 1 Rue de Varembé, Geneva, Switzerland

34 BS 5490: 1977 *Specification for degree of protection provided by enclosures* BSI

35 BS 4293:1983 *Specification for residual current-operated circuit-breakers* BSI

36 HSE Guidance Note PM 38 *Selection and use of electric handlamps* ISBN 0 11 883582 3 HMSO

37 BS 3535: 1962 *Specification for safety isolating transformers for industrial and domestic purposes* BSI

38 HSE Guidance Note PM 32 *The safe use of portable electrical apparatus (electrical safety)* ISBN 0 11 883563 7 HMSO

39 BS 5345: Part I: 1976 *Code of Practice for the selection, installation and maintenance of electrical apparatus for use in potentially explosive atmospheres basic requirements for all parts of the Code* ISBN 0 580 09414 6 BSI

40 BS 5345: Part II: 1983 *Classification of Hazardous Areas* BSI

41 HSE Guidance booklet HS(G)22 *Electrical apparatus for use in potentially explosive atmospheres* ISBN 0 11 883746 X HMSO

42 HSC leaflet HSC6 (revised) *Writing a safety policy statement - advice to employers* Available free from HSE

43 HSE booklet *Writing Your health and safety policy statement - how to prepare a safety policy statement for small business* ISBN 0 11 883882 2 HMSO

44 *The Health and Safety (First Aid) Regulations 1981* SI 1981 No 917 ISBN 0 11 016917 4 HMSO

45 HSE booklet HS(R)11, *First aid at work* ISBN 0 11 8834460 HMSO

46 HSE leaflet IND(G) 32(L) *Watch your step - prevention of slipping, tripping and falling accidents at work* HMSO

47 BS 4211: 1987 *Specification for ladders for permanent access to chimneys, other high structures, silos and bins* BSI

48 HSE Guidance Note GS 15 *General access scaffolds* ISBN 0 11 883545 9 HMSO

49 HSE Guidance Note GS 42 *Tower scaffolds* ISBN 0 11 883941 1 HMSO

50 HSE Guidance Note GS 31 *Safe use of ladders, step ladders and trestles* ISBN 0 11 883594 7 HMSO

51 HSE Guidance Note GS 10 *Roofwork: prevention of falls* ISBN 0 11 883195 X HMSO

52 *Construction (General Provisions) Regulations 1961* SI 1961 No 1580 ISBN 0 11 100143 9 as amended by SI 1966 No 94 and SI 1974 No 16816 ISBN 0 11 041681 3 HMSO

53 *Construction (Lifting Operations) Regulations 1961* SI 1961 No 1581 HMSO

54 *Construction (Working Places) Regulations 1966* SI 1966 No 94 HMSO

55 *Construction (Health and Welfare) Regulations 1966* SI 1966 No 95 HMSO

56 HSE booklet *Deadly maintenance - roofs, a study of fatal accidents at work* ISNB 0 11 883804 0 HMSO

57 BS 6230: *Specification for installation of gas-fired, forced convection air heaters for commercial and industrial space heating of rated input exceeding 60KW (second family gases)* BSI

58 British Standards Code of Practice BSCP 341: 300-307: 1956 *Central heating by low pressure hot water* BSI

59 BS 759: Part 1: 1984, *Specification for valves, mountings and fittings* Part 2: 1975 (obsolescent) *Safety valves* BSI

60 BS 779: 1976 *Cast iron boilers for central heating and indirect water supply (44 kW rating and above)* BSI

61 BS 799 Pts 2-6 *Oil burning equipment* BSI

62 BS 855: 1976 *Specification for welded steel boilers for central heating and indirect hot water supply (rated output 44 kW to 3 MW)* BSI

63 BS 1113: 1985 *Specification for design and manufacture of water-tube steam generating plant (including super heaters, reheaters and steel tube economisers)* BSI

64 BS 1374: 1972 *Recommendations on the use of British Standard Log Sheets for steam and hot water boiler plants* BSI

65 BS 1971: 1969 *Corrugated furnaces for shell boilers* BSI

66 BS 2486: 1978 *Recommendations for treatment of water for land boilers* BSI

67 BS 2790 *Specification for shell boilers of welded construction* BSI

68 BS 4433: Pts 1 and 2 *Solid smokeless fuel boilers with rated outputs up to 45 kW* BSI

69 BS 6798: 1987 *Specification for installation of gas-fired water boilers of rated input not exceeding 60 kW* BSI

70 BS 5410, Pts 1-3 *Code of Practice for oil firing* BSI

71 BS 5440, Pts 1 and 2 *Code of Practice for flues and air supply for gas appliances of rated input not exceeding 60 kW (1st and 2nd family gases)* BSI

72 BS 5885: 1980 *Specification for industrial gas burners of input rating 60 kW and above* BSI

73 BS 5978, Pts 1-3 *Safety and performance of gas-fired hot water boilers (60 kW to 2 MW input)* BSI

74 HSE Guidance Note GS 5 *Entry into confined spaces* ISBN 0 11 883067 8 HMSO

75 DoE booklet *Asbestos materials in buildings* ISBN 0 11 751890 5 HMSO

76 *Control of Asbestos at Work Regulations 1987* SI 1987 No 2155 ISBN 0 11 078115 5 HMSO

77 HSC Approved Code of Practice COP 3 *Work with asbestos insulation, asbestos coating and asbestos insulating board* (in support of SI 1969 No 69 and the general duties of the HSW Act 1974) ISBN 0 11 883979 0 HMSO

78 HSC Approved Code of Practice and Guidance Note *Work with asbestos insulation and asbestos coating (Revised February 1985)* ISBN 0 11 883797 4 HMSO

79 *The Asbestos (Licensing) Regulations 1983* SI 1983 No 1649 ISBN 0 11 037649 8 HMSO

80 HSE Guidance Note GS 25 *Prevention of falls to window cleaners* ISBN 0 11 883573 4 HMSO

81 DoE booklet *The purification of swimming pool water* HMSO 1975, reprinted 1980

82 DoE booklet *The treatment and quality of swimming pool water* ISBN 0 11 751757 7 HMSO 1984

83 DoE booklet *Swimming pool disinfection systems using sodium hypochlorite and calcium hypochlorite - a survey of the efficacy of disinfection* HMSO 1982

84 DoE booklet *Swimming pool disinfection systems using chloroisocyanurates - a survey of the efficacy of disinfection* HMSO 1982

85 DoE booklet *Swimming pool disinfection systems using ozone with residual chlorination - monitoring the efficacy of disinfection* HMSO 1982

86 DoE booklet *Swimming pool disinfection systems using electrolytically generated sodium hypochlorite - monitoring the efficacy of disinfection* HMSO 1983

87 DoE booklet *Swimming pool disinfection systems using chlorine gas - guidelines for design and operation* HMSO 1979

88 DoE booklet *Swimming pool disinfection systems using sodium hypochlorite - guidelines for design and operation* HMSO 1979

89 DoE booklet *Swimming pool disinfection systems using ozone with residual free chlorine or electrolytic generation of hypochlorite - guidelines for design and operation* HMSO 1982

90 DoE booklet *Swimming pool disinfection systems using elemental liquid bromine - guidelines for design and operation* HMSO 1981

91 DOE booklet *Swimming pool disinfection systems using calcium hypochlorite, chloroisocyanurates, halogenated dimethylhydantoins and solid ancillary chemicals - guidelines for design and operation* HMSO 1981

92 *The Classification, Packaging and Labelling of Dangerous Substances Regulations 1984* SI 1984 No 1244 HMSO

93 BS 2092: 1967 *Specification for industrial eye-protectors* BSI

94 BS 5426: 1976 *Specification for workwear* BSI

95 BS 4275: 1974 *Recommendations for the selection, use and maintenance of respiratory protective equipment* BSI

96 BS 2091: 1969 *Respirators for protection against harmful dust, gases and scheduled agricultural chemicals* BSI

97 *Notification of Installations Handling Hazardous Substances Regulations 1982* SI 1982 No 1357 ISBN 0 11 027357 5 HMSO

98 *Control of Industrial Major Accident Hazards Regulations 1984* SI 1984 No 1902 ISBN 0 11 047902 5 HMSO

99 British Effluent and Water Association and Pool Water Treatment Advisory Group *Code of Practice for ozone plant for swimming pool water treatment* ISBN 0 95 099791 9 BEWA 1987

100 Pool Water Treatment Advisory Group: *Ozone water treatment for swimming pools - A national survey* ISBN 0 90 657771 3 Sports Council, 1986 Available from address at ref 3

101 HSE Guidance Note EH 38 *Ozone: health hazards and precautionary measures* ISBN 0 11 883562 9 HMSO

102 HSE Guidance Note EH 40 *Occupational exposure limits* published annually HMSO

103 DoE circular 72/78; Welsh Office circular 102/78; Scottish Education Department Circular 1039/79 *Statement on the use of chlorine gas in the treatment of water of swimming pools* HMSO

104 HSE Guidance booklet HS(G) 40 *Chlorine from drums and cylinders* ISBN 0 11 883968 3 HMSO

105 HSE Guidance Note CS 9 *Bulk storage and use of liquid carbon dioxide: hazards and procedures* ISBN 0 11 883513 0 HMSO

106 Sports Council/TUS Energy Data Sheet No 1 *Swimming pool covers* Available free from address at ref 3

107 DES Safety Series No 4 (Revised 1978) *Safety in physical education* ISBN 0 11 270320 8 HMSO

108 British Association of Advisers and Lecturers in Physical Education *Safe practice in physical education* Obtainable from Mr C P Smith, Abbotsfield, Ferry Lane, Medmenham, Marlow on Thames, Bucks SL7 2E7 - price 3.50 per copy inc p + p. (Please make checques payable to BAALPE)

109 *Use of play equipment in swimming pools - A suggeted code of practice* Obtainable from the Institute of Baths and Recreation Management, Giffard House, 36/38 Sherrard Street, Melton Mowbray, Leicestershire, LE13 1XJ

110 HSE booklet HS(R)7 *A guide to the Safety Signs Regulations 1980* ISBN 0 11 883415 0 HMSO

111 HSE booklet HSE 11 (rev) *Reporting an injury or a dangerous occurrence* available free from HSE

112 HSE booklet HS(R)23 *A guide to the Reporting of Injuries, Diseases or Dangerous Occurrences Regulations* ISBN 0 11 883858 X HMSO